CW00552713

THE "NEXT STAGE" GUITAR ~~BOOK~~
Learn How To Play Scale Patterns & Tabs Easily & ~~Quickly~~

Created By...C. F. Lopez, Jr. 'Chris'

Welcome to *The "Next Stage" Guitar Book!* This guitar book contains a simple learning method that will help you master the skill of playing basic musical scales quickly and easily without having to learn anything about music theory. Most of the scales presented are **MAJOR SCALES**, the familiar **Do-Re-Me-Fa-Sol-La-Ti-Do** that most of us have heard since childhood. The last half of the book will introduce you to the **PENTATONIC SCALES** (both Major & Minor) and **"THE BLUES SCALE."**

The material presented is designed so you will not be at all overwhelmed with more scales and information than you need to know during this early stage of your musical development. However, enough fundamental scales are presented, in an easy to understand format, so that you can develop your musical skills and move on to the next level of instruction.

Each new scale is presented in three ways; **(1) "Scale Path"** diagram, **(2) "Standard Music Notation"** and **(3) "Tablature"** for that particular scale. If you like, you may record the scales you are learning and play them back periodically to monitor your progress.

You will discover that by playing and memorizing these scales, you are preparing yourself for more advance scales and musical concepts. Knowledge is power, and once you unlock the "secret" to playing scales, you can create your own phrasings and melodic patterns.

The key to mastering scales is consistent practice and repetition. It is critical that you **MEMORIZE** the scales as they are presented. The more you practice the scales, the easier they become to play from memory.

Copyright © 1999, 2001 by Christopher Winkle Products
All Rights Reserved

New & Revised July 2001

ISBN 0-9667719-2-3

Printed in the United States of America

The "Next Stage" Guitar Book
Learn How To Play Scale Patterns & Tabs Easily & Quickly!

Acknowledgement

Special thanks to Russ Hucek, President of Kradl, Inc., maker of the new and the uniquely designed KRADL® Guitar Picks, for his contributions and professionalism in guitar playing and instruction techniques.

www.KRADL.com

Book Cover Design
Lyndon Vasquez
E-mail: studiolv@hotmail.com

THE "NEXT STAGE" GUITAR BOOK
Learn How To Play Scale Patterns & Tabs Easily & Quickly!

TABLE OF CONTENTS

Christopher Winkle Products
P.O. Box 1898, Lomita, California 90717
USA
E-mail: quickstartguitar@msn.com

Frequently Asked Questions

* ### Do I have to be able to read music to play scales?

No! Being able to read music is **NOT** necessary. You can learn the scales from the **"Scale Path"** Diagrams, or from the easy to read **Tablature.**

* ### Do I have to read all these pages of text, or can I start by playing scales first?

No! You don't have to read all the text. But I would highly recommend doing so. If you read nothing else, I would recommend that **EVERYONE** read the section on **"Standard And Optional Fingering."**

* ### Do I have to learn each scale in the order that is presented in the book?

No! You can start any place in the book you wish. The advantage of starting at the beginning of the book is that it provides an organized method for grouping scales that begin on the same string.

* ### Do I have to know anything about Music Theory?

Not a thing. Although we tried to avoid as much Music Theory as possible, we found that it is nearly impossible to discuss some topics without at least mentioning something about "Music Theory 101."

GETTING STARTED

Before getting started with the scales, I have included some general information about the guitar and how to understand the chord diagrams that are included toward the back of this book. If you are already familiar with some of the information presented, skip those sections and go to a topic you are not familiar with.

*   **Tuning The Guitar:** The best way to tune the guitar is by using any number of quality pitch pipes, tuning forks or battery powered guitar tuners which are available at many fine music stores.

*   **Guitar Picks:** For beginners, a light or medium gauge (thickness) pick is suggested because they offer more flexibility (and less resistance) when strumming chords. Hold the pick in such a manner so that the tip of the pick points slightly upward when strumming downward across the strings. Conversely, when strumming upward, allow the tip of the pick to aim slightly downward.

*   **Positioning The Guitar:** Rest the curve section (the waist) at side of the guitar comfortably on the lap of your right leg, behind your knee. Hold the neck up in a slight angle with the left hand.

*   **Positioning The Left Hand On The Guitar Neck:** Grab the guitar neck with the left hand so that the thumb is positioned directly behind the neck and resting comfortably against it. Your fingers tips should be resting on the strings. Avoid "choking" the neck with excessive force. Try to keep your left hand relaxed.

GETTING STARTED

*   **Positioning The Fingers On The Guitar Neck:** Press left hand finger **TIPS** near (but NOT on) the frets (the fret wire) when playing scales and chords. Apply a firm, downward pressure against the strings. It is important that you use your **FINGER TIPS** when playing and **NOT** the fleshly part of your finger that lies between the tip of your finger and the first knuckle. Finger tips may become sore at first, but this discomfort will lessen with time and practice.

*   **Picking Notes In A Scale:** Scales are played by picking single notes. For beginners, it is perfectly acceptable to pick all your scale notes with a downward motion of the guitar pick. More advanced players will learn a technique called **"Alternate Picking,"** whereby the pick moves in an alternating pattern against the single string(s), so that each note of the scale is played with the pick moving in the opposite direction (i.e., the first note is picked down, the second is picked up, the third is picked down....etc.).

*   **Strumming The Strings:** Strumming is the technique used to play chords (three or more notes) with the pick. To begin the strum, start with the lower (in pitch) or heavier strings at the top, as you look down at your guitar. While you hold a chord with your left hand, strum downward across all the strings in the chord. Slowly, or at a speed that is comfortable for you, practice strumming **each** chord at least four (4) times. Practice keeping time by tapping your foot and counting to four (1 anna, 2 anna, 3 anna, 4, etc.). Every time you count the "number," a strum should coincide with your foot tapping the floor. The "anna" should coincide with your foot completely raised off the floor. Once the downward strum is mastered, practice a strum that uses both the downward strum and an upward strum. In this instance, the downward strum "plays" the "numbered" count and the upward strum "plays" the "anna" count.

HOW TO TUNE YOUR GUITAR

The best way to tune the guitar is by using any number of quality pitch pipes, tuning forks or battery powered guitar tuners which are available at any fine music store.

It is critical that you keep and play your guitar "in tune." Another important, but often overlooked point, is to learn which tuning peg tunes which string, and the direction you have to turn the pegs to raise and lower the pitch of the strings. Learning this very mechanical aspect of the guitar will save you much time and confusion now and in the future. One last fine point about tuning; always tune your guitar so that you are **raising** the pitch to the correct note. That is to say, you should be **tightening** the strings as you tune your guitar, as opposed to loosening the strings, to achieve the desired note. This practice eliminates "slippage" or the slack that occurs when tension on a string(s) is lessened, causing the string to quickly go out of tune again.

*Please, take note of the arrows in the diagram on the following page. One end of the arrow points to the note which is to be held down (with the second finger) during the tuning process. The other end of the same arrow points to the open string which will be tuned to the note that is being held down at the opposite end of the arrow.

HOW TO TUNE YOUR GUITAR

BELOW THE DIAGRAMS ARE THE STRING NOTE NAMES AND THE CORRESPONDING STRING NUMBERS.
* BEGIN BY TUNING THE 6TH STRING-THE OPEN LOW "E" NOTE (TO A LOW "E" NOTE PITCH)

"OPEN" MEANS:
THE STRING IS NOT PRESSED DOWN

PLACE YOUR MIDDLE FINGER AND PRESS DOWN ON THE 5TH FRET-6TH STRING, STRIKE THIS NOTE (THIS IS AN "A" NOTE). NEXT, STRIKE THE OPEN 5TH STRING (THE OPEN "A" NOTE STRING), TUNE THE OPEN "A" NOTE STRING TO THE PITCH OF THE NOTE BEING HELD DOWN WITH YOUR FINGER.
BOTH STRINGS SHOULD MATCH IN PITCH.
(TO AN "A" NOTE PITCH)

PLACE YOUR MIDDLE FINGER AND PRESS DOWN ON THE 5TH FRET- 5TH STRING, STRIKE THIS NOTE (THIS IS A "D" NOTE). NEXT, STRIKE THE OPEN 4TH STRING (THE OPEN "D" NOTE STRING), TUNE THE OPEN "D" NOTE STRING TO THE PITCH OF THE NOTE BEING HELD DOWN WITH YOUR FINGER.
BOTH STRINGS SHOULD MATCH IN PITCH.
(TO A "D" NOTE PITCH)

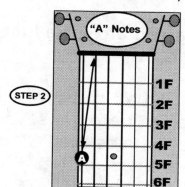

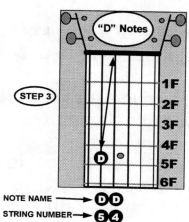

PLACE YOUR MIDDLE FINGER AND PRESS DOWN ON THE 5TH FRET-4TH STRING, STRIKE THIS NOTE (THIS IS A "G" NOTE). NEXT, STRIKE THE OPEN 3RD STRING (THE OPEN "G" NOTE STRING), TUNE THE OPEN "G" NOTE STRING TO THE PITCH OF THE NOTE BEING HELD DOWN WITH YOUR FINGER.
BOTH STRINGS SHOULD MATCH IN PITCH.
(TO A "G" NOTE PITCH)

PLACE YOUR MIDDLE FINGER AND PRESS DOWN ON THE 4TH FRET-3RD STRING, STRIKE THIS NOTE (THIS IS A "B" NOTE). NEXT, STRIKE THE OPEN 2ND STRING (THE OPEN "B" NOTE STRING), TUNE THE OPEN "B" NOTE STRING TO THE PITCH OF THE NOTE BEING HELD DOWN WITH YOUR FINGER.
BOTH STRINGS SHOULD MATCH IN PITCH.
(TO A "B" NOTE PITCH)

PLACE YOUR MIDDLE FINGER AND PRESS DOWN ON THE 5TH FRET-2ND STRING, STRIKE THIS NOTE (THIS IS AN "E" NOTE). NEXT, STRIKE THE OPEN 1ST STRING (THE OPEN "E" NOTE STRING), TUNE THE OPEN "E" NOTE STRING TO THE PITCH OF THE NOTE BEING HELD DOWN WITH YOUR FINGER.
BOTH STRINGS SHOULD MATCH IN PITCH.
(TO AN "E" NOTE HIGH PITCH)

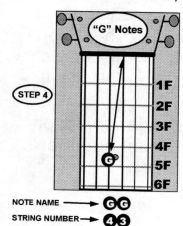

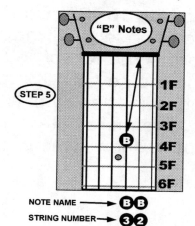

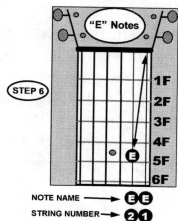

THE STAFF & NOTE NAMES

Standard musical notation is written on a **"Staff."** The staff is comprised of five (5) horizontal lines and four (4) horizontal spaces between the five lines. These lines and spaces make up the staff where music notation or notes are written.

There are seven (7) notes named after the first seven (7) letters of the alphabet **(A-B-C-D-E-F-G).**

To determine the name and pitch of the notes, a clef sign is placed at the very beginning of the staff. There are several different clefs for various instruments. The guitar uses the **"G"** or **Treble Clef.** The treble (G) clef resembles an ampersand ("&").

This is technical stuff, but notes can be played "Natural" (A - B - C - D - E - F - G), or notes can be altered from there natural state. That is to say a note(s) can be raised or "sharpened" (#) above its natural position. Conversely, the same note(s) can be lowered or "flattened" (♭) below its natural position. The **Key Signature** (we will discuss this soon enough), with the use of sharps and flats, will determine what "key" a scale (or song) is in. The **Key Signature** is the area immediatley to the **RIGHT** of the **Treble ("G") Clef.** The absence of sharps or flats means the scale is written in the Key of "C" Major (or A minor, a "related" key to "C" major). The presence of sharps or flats means the scale or song is written in a key other than the Key of "C" (i.e., one sharp = the Key of "G," one flat = the Key of "F"). If the song is written in the Key of "G," then **ALL** your "F's" will be sharp. If the song is written in the Key of "F," then **ALL** your "B's" will be flat. Other Keys will have more notes that are either sharp or flat. The staff on the next page shows where the individual notes are located on the guitar.

THE STAFF & NOTE NAMES

Hint: Remember that the **LINE NOTES** on the staff use the first letter of each word in the saying: "**E**very **G**ood **B**oy **D**oes **F**ine" (E-G-B-D-F), while the **SPACE NOTES** on the staff spell the word **"Face"** (F-A-C-E). You will also notice that any given note can and does reside on both the Lines and Spaces (i.e., "E" is a line note in "**E**very Good Boy Does Fine" and a space note in "FAC**E**").

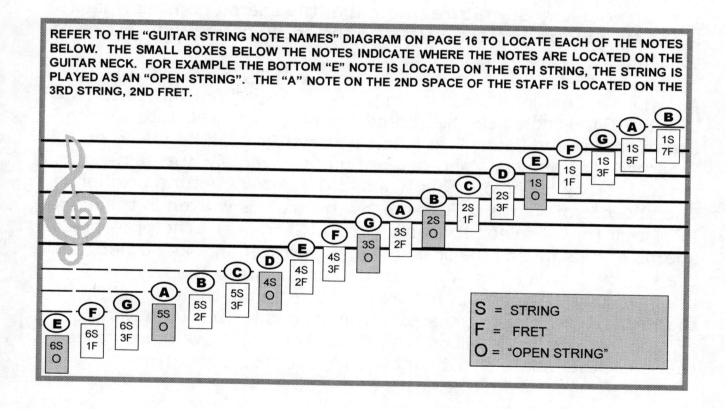

REFER TO THE "GUITAR STRING NOTE NAMES" DIAGRAM ON PAGE 16 TO LOCATE EACH OF THE NOTES BELOW. THE SMALL BOXES BELOW THE NOTES INDICATE WHERE THE NOTES ARE LOCATED ON THE GUITAR NECK. FOR EXAMPLE THE BOTTOM "E" NOTE IS LOCATED ON THE 6TH STRING, THE STRING IS PLAYED AS AN "OPEN STRING". THE "A" NOTE ON THE 2ND SPACE OF THE STAFF IS LOCATED ON THE 3RD STRING, 2ND FRET.

S = STRING
F = FRET
O = "OPEN STRING"

KEY SIGNATURES

Some **Keys** will have certain notes that are played either sharp or flat throughout most, if not all, of the musical piece unless otherwise indicated. Rather than place a sharp or flat symbol before each individual note in the composition, we can indicate which notes are sharp or flat at the very beginning of the piece. We use the **Key Signature** to tell us what notes are natural, what notes are sharp and what notes are flat. The number of sharps and flats (or lack thereof) will determine what "key" the music is to be played. The **Key Signature** is located on the first bar of the staff immediately to the right of the **Treble Clef** (the symbol that looks like **"&"**). The key of a particular piece of music can be easily determined by the number or sharps or flats contained in the **Key Signature**. Note that the sharp and flat symbol(s) in the **Key Signature** are written on the space or line that relates to that note.

As we stated earlier, notes can be played in their "natural" state (A-B-C-D-E-F-G), or notes can be altered from their natural state with the use of sharps and flats. That is to say, a note(s) can be raised or "sharped" (#) above its natural position. Conversely, the same note(s) can be lowered or "flattened" (♭) below its natural position. The absence of sharps or flats means the scale is written in the key of "C" Major (or "A" minor, a related key to "C" major). The presence of sharps or flats means the scale or song is written in a key other than the Key of "C" major or "A" minor (i.e., one sharp = the key of "G," one flat = the key of "F"). If the song is written in the Key of "G," then **ALL** your F's will be sharp. If the song is written in the Key of "F," then **ALL** your B's will be flat. Other keys will have more notes that are either sharp or flat contained in the **Key Signature.**

There are some mental short-cuts to tell one key from another, but in the long run, memorizing each **Key Signature** is probably the best method I know.

KEY SIGNATURES

15

GUITAR STRING NOTE NAMES

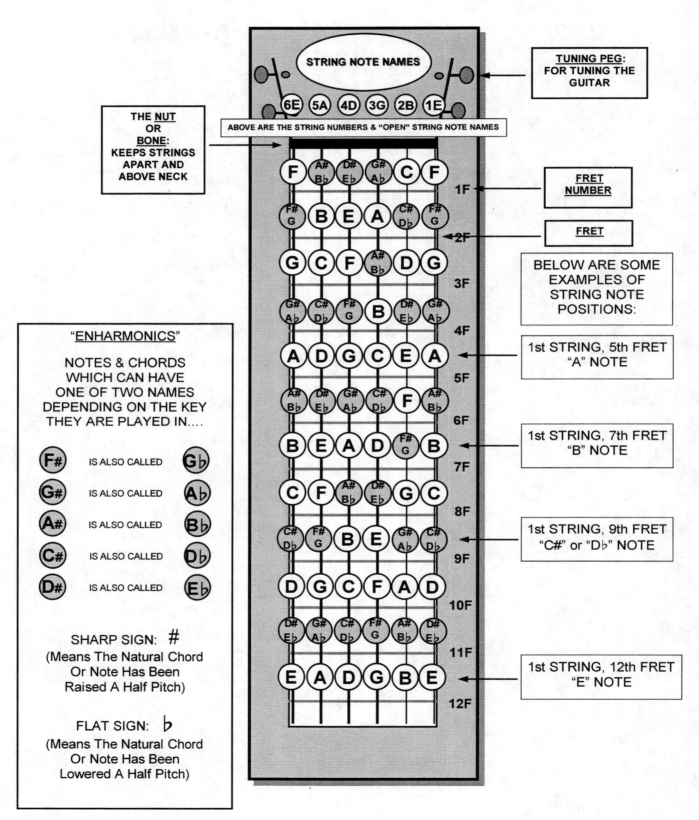

STRING NOTE NAMES

TUNING PEG: FOR TUNING THE GUITAR

6E 5A 4D 3G 2B 1E

ABOVE ARE THE STRING NUMBERS & "OPEN" STRING NOTE NAMES

THE **NUT** OR **BONE:** KEEPS STRINGS APART AND ABOVE NECK

FRET NUMBER

FRET

BELOW ARE SOME EXAMPLES OF STRING NOTE POSITIONS:

1st STRING, 5th FRET "A" NOTE

1st STRING, 7th FRET "B" NOTE

1st STRING, 9th FRET "C#" or "Db" NOTE

1st STRING, 12th FRET "E" NOTE

"ENHARMONICS"

NOTES & CHORDS WHICH CAN HAVE ONE OF TWO NAMES DEPENDING ON THE KEY THEY ARE PLAYED IN....

F#   IS ALSO CALLED   Gb

G#   IS ALSO CALLED   Ab

A#   IS ALSO CALLED   Bb

C#   IS ALSO CALLED   Db

D#   IS ALSO CALLED   Eb

SHARP SIGN: #
(Means The Natural Chord Or Note Has Been Raised A Half Pitch)

FLAT SIGN: b
(Means The Natural Chord Or Note Has Been Lowered A Half Pitch)

16

UNDERSTANDING SCALES

A scale is an ascending or descending series of predetermined pitches (tone/notes) performed in relationship to a **specific pattern** of **intervals** between notes. This is important, because it is the specific pattern of intervals that gives each scale its unique sound. A scale can begin on any given letter of the musical alphabet **(i.e., A, B, C, D, E, F, G),** including the sharp and flat notes of each of these notes.

INTERVALS

An **Interval** is the distance between any two tones/pitches (i.e., two different notes). They can be **Half Steps** (also called **Semi-Tones**) or **Whole Steps**. **Intervals** can be even larger than a **Whole Step**. **Half Step** intervals on the guitar are two (2) distinct notes that reside on adjacent frets to one another (frets that are side-by-side to one another or an open note to a first fret note). Thus, the distance from the open "E" note on the first string to the "F" note on the first fret of the same string is an example of a **Half Step**. The frets on the guitar fingerboard, in fact, are a series of **Half** or **Semi-Tones** to the fret(s) or notes on either side of them.

A **Whole Step** on the guitar are two (2) distinct notes that require the distance of three (adjacent) frets, or the distance from an open note to a note on the second fret of the same string. Another way to view a **Whole Step** is a note that is either two (2) frets above or below any given note on the same string. Thus, the distance from an "F" note on the 1st string, 1st fret, to the "G" note on the 3rd fret of the 1st string would be an example of a **Whole Step**. This is good to know but not necessary in order to play scales.

If you are fortunate enough to have a piano at your disposal, you can easily see and play the **Half** and **Whole Steps**. If you look at the white keys on the piano, you will notice that all the keys have black keys between them except for four (4) white keys that have no black keys between them. Two adjacent white keys with a **BLACK KEY** in between is a **Whole Step**. A white key to an adjacent white key without **BLACK KEY** in between is a **Half-Step**. It is just that simple.

HOW TO CREATE A MAJOR (Diatonic) SCALE

A **Major Scale** is created with a predetermined pattern of intervals between adjacent notes (that's why we had to explain what an **"Interval"** was). A **Major Scale** is comprised of eight **(8)** notes, starting with the note name of the **Major Scale** you wish to play (also called the **"Root"**) and ending on the same note one octave higher than the starting note of the scale.

Here is the **"Formula"** that is used to create a **Major Scale**:

Whole - Whole - Half - Whole - Whole - Whole - Half

In some other books a **Whole-Step** could be represented with a **"W"** or a **"1"**. Similarly, **Half-Steps** will be represented with an **"H"**, **"S"** (semi-tone) or a **"1/2"**.

So if we want to create a **"C" Major Scale**, we start with a **"C"** note and write down **EVERY** note (alphabetically) of the musical alphabet until we come to the next **"C"** note.

Example: C - D - E - F - G - A - B - C

If we analyze the **Intervals** of the notes, we have a **Whole-Step** between **C** and **D**, a **Whole-Step** between **D** and **E**, a **Half-Step** between **E** and **F**, a **Whole-Step** between **F** and **G**, a **Whole-Step** between **G** and **A**, a **Whole-Step** between **A** and **B** and a **Half-Step** between **B** and **C**. Just like our Major Scale formula.

HOW TO CREATE MAJOR (Diatonic) SCALE
(Visual Example)

Below is a visual example of how the "C" Major Scale is created using the Major Scale formula explained on the previous page:

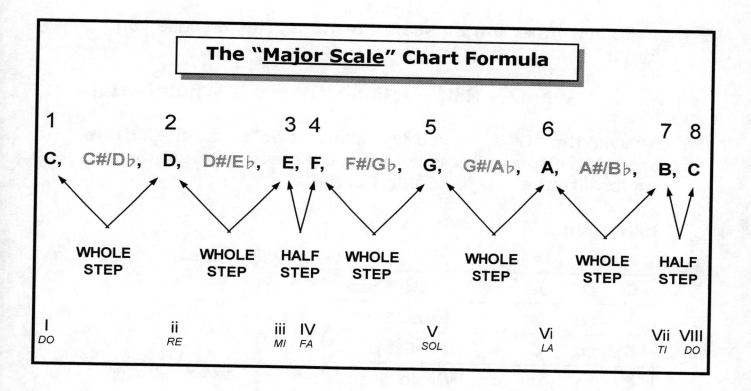

Again, the notes which form the **"C" Major Scale** are:

C - D - E - F - G - A - B - C

HOW TO CREATE A MAJOR (Diatonic) SCALE

If we wanted to create a **"G"** Major Scale we would follow these five (5) steps:

1.) Write down the eight notes in the musical alphabet starting with **"G"** and ending with the next **"G":**
   Example G - A - B - C - D - E - F - G

2.) Write down the **"Major Scale Formula"** (just in case you forget):

   Whole - Whole - Half - Whole - Whole - Whole - Half

3.) Analyze the **"G"** scale you just wrote down to see the **Whole** and **Half-Step** patterns before you adjust or correct them to conform to the **"Major Scale Formula."**

   Example:

G	to	A	=	Whole Step
A	to	B	=	Whole Step
B	to	C	=	Half Step
C	to	D	=	Whole Step
D	to	E	=	Whole Step
E	to	F	=	Half Step
F	to	G	=	Whole Step

You will notice that everything follows the **"Formula"** until we get to **"E to F = Half Step"** and the **"F to G = Whole Step."** These should be a **Whole Step** and **Half-Step,** respectively.

HOW TO CREATE A MAJOR (Diatonic) SCALE

4.) Adjust your notes so that the intervals match the major scale formula. To solve this problem, we have to adjust or correct the **"F"** note first. In this case we have to "push" the **"F"** note away from the **"E"** by sharping the **"F,"** making it an **F#.** This **increases** that **interval** from a **Half-Step** to a **Whole-Step.** At the same time, we **decreased** the **interval** between the **"F"** and the **"G"** notes to a **Half-Step** when we "pushed" the **"F"** closer to the **"G"** when we sharp the **F** to an **F#.**

5.) Re-analyze your "corrected" note intervals. Now our **"G"** scale matches the **"Major Scale Formula"**:

G - A - B - C - D - E - F# - G

Example:

G	**to**	**A**	**=**	**Whole Step**
A	**to**	**B**	**=**	**Whole Step**
B	**to**	**C**	**=**	**Half Step**
C	**to**	**D**	**=**	**Whole Step**
D	**to**	**E**	**=**	**Whole Step**
E	**to**	**F#**	**=**	**Whole Step**
F#	**to**	**G**	**=**	**Half Step**

To create a Major Scale for any other key, just repeat the five (5) steps.

HOW TO READ THE SCALES USING THE SCALE PATH DIAGRAM, STANDARD NOTATION & TABLATURE

As we stated earlier, this book is divided into three parts. **Part I** will concentrate primarily on single octave **"Major (Diatonic) Scales."** **"Diatonic"** is a fancy sounding word that means the scale relates to a standard major (or minor) scale with eight (8) tones and no deviations in the **"formula"** (intervals). **Part II** we cover double octave **"Major (Diatonic) Scales."** In **Part III** we included **"Major Pentatonic," "Minor Pentatonic"** and the ever popular **"Blues Scale,"** along with some simple chord progressions so you can get an idea on how all this "stuff" fits together.

We have given each scale a **"Pattern Name."** Basically, the **"Pattern Name"** is a method we devised to easily identify and organize each pattern. The **"Pattern Name"** is comprised of a regular (Arabic) **NUMBER** (6 through 3) to indicate what string plays the first ("root") note of the scale, followed by a **hyphen** and a **ROMAN NUMERAL** to differentiate scales that all begin on the same string. Thus, **"3-II"** means that the scales begins on the third (3rd) string, and it is the second (2nd) scale pattern to begin on that string. It's that simple. Once you memorize the scales, the **"Pattern Names"** become less and less important. We begin by showing you scales starting on the sixth (6th) string and proceeding on each successive string until we get to the third (3rd) string.

1. "SCALE PATH" DIAGRAM:

This method is best described as the **"One Picture Paints A Thousand Words"** method. Each scale is symbolically drawn on an illustrated picture of a guitar neck. A small circle(s) depicted on the fret(s) tells us where on the fingerboard we play the notes of the scale. We will call this small circle(s) the **"Finger/Note Identifier"** because it tells us the correct finger to use and the name of the note.

The fret numbers are indicated along the right side of the scale path diagram (i.e., 1F, 2F, 3F....etc.). You should begin playing the scales (see **"Scale Path"**) starting with the "root" note. The root note will be the lowest pitched note on the **LEFT** side of the **"Scale Path"** diagram. The root note(s) will also be "colored" **GRAY** so you can easily identify them from the other notes in the scale. From that gray colored root note, proceed in (alphabetical) order through each successively higher note on each string until you reach the final or highest pitch root note in the scale (it too will be "colored" **GRAY**) on the **RIGHT** side of the **"Scale Path"** diagram. To descend, just reverse the process.

Another way to view this process is to think that the scales always (for now) start on the heavier gauge strings and move toward the lighter or thinner gauge strings, then reverse and proceed back to the beginning.

STANDARD & OPTIONAL FINGERING

Most scales only have one fingering configuration for both the ascending and descending forms of the scale. We can call this **Standard Fingering,** for lack of a better word. Other scales, however, can be played with more than one fingering configuration, even though the basic scale pattern remains the same. In these instances, we included a scale with the same **"Scale Path"** and **"Pattern Name,"** but with an **"Optional Fingering"** for you to use. The **"Optional Fingering"** will be on the page immediately following the first fingering configuration provided in the book and it will be clearly labeled as **"Optional Fingering"** in the page heading.

When playing a scale with **"Optional Fingering,"** the <u>**descending form of the scale will use different fingers to execute the scale on some (not all) of the notes in place of the fingers used in the ascending form of the same scale**</u>. You will see in the **"Scale Path"** diagrams, numbers that look like **"FRACTIONS"** inside the circle of the **"Finger/Note Identifier"** on the frets. The same **"fractions"** appear in the fingering numbers in the oval shape circles on the **Tablature.** In reality, what these **"fractions"** represent are **Ascending Fingers** and **Descending Fingers.** The **TOP** number represents fingers to be used when playing an ascending scale (from the lowest pitch to the highest pitched note). The number on the **BOTTOM** represents fingers to be used when playing a descending scale (from the highest pitch note to the lowest pitch note). This **Fraction** convention is also used in **Standard** fingering **Pattern 6-III** (6-III has no optional fingering but uses a **FRACTION** just the same).

For example:

Use 2nd Finger To Ascend > $\left(\dfrac{2}{1}\right)$ Use 4th Finger To Ascend > $\left(\dfrac{4}{3}\right)$
Use 1st Finger To Descend >   Use 3rd Finger To Descend >

All scales should be **MEMORIZED** with the **FINGERING** as shown on the guitar neck **"Scale Path"** or with the bold **FRET NUMBER** and **OVAL SHAPED FINGER IDENTIFIER** as shown on the **"Tablature."**

2. STANDARD MUSICAL NOTATION:

If you can read "standard musical notation," you may find that is an ideal place to start. Again, all scales begin in the ascending mode; that is, the first note (the root note) of the scale will be the lowest note in terms of pitch and proceed in sequence (alphabetically) until the highest note of the scale is reached. The notes on the staff are in relationship to the **"Finger/Note Identifiers"** (numbers & notes) on the **"Scale Path"** and the oval **"Finger Identifiers"** depicted in the **Tablature** directly below the Staff.

3. TABLATURE:

If reading music is not your "cup of tea," you can utilize the **Tablature** provided to play the scales. Although tablature carries a strong resemblance to standard musical notation, that is where the similarities end. Each horizontal line of the **"Tab"** (Tablature) represents a string on the guitar - **NOT DEGREES OF PITCH** (i.e., notes on a staff) as presented in standard notation. That is why tablature has six (6) horizontal lines (strings 1 through 6), while standard notation on the staff uses five (5) lines. The top line on the tablature represents the first string on the guitar and proceeds in sequence to the sixth string on the bottom of the tablature.

Tablature also differs from standard notation in that tablature incorporates the use of **NUMBERS,** rather than notes to identify a specific note or notes to be played on the guitar. Thus, a number **"4"** placed on the top line (1st string) of the **Tab** means; **press down on the (4th) fret of the first (1st) string on the guitar fingerboard and play (pluck) the first (1st) string.** Similarly, a **"0"** placed on the top line (1st string) of the **Tab** means; **play (pluck) the first (1st) string open on the guitar (no fingering on the frets).**

To indicate which fingers to use, we placed a small oval shape **"Finger Identifier,"** with the correct finger(s), next to the **BOLD** fret number. Directly above the **Tablature** you will find the same corresponding note(s) written in standard musical notation.

MOVABLE SCALE PATTERNS:

The beautiful feature of the scales, as presented in this book, is that they are **ALL "Movable Scales."** That is to say you can change to a different scale other than the one illustrated on the page (i.e., "A" Major Scale to a "G" Major Scale). This can be accomplished by simply starting any of the **"Scale Patterns"** on a different fret or root note other than the one depicted in the book. Nothing changes other than the frets (and the notes) that the original scale was played on. Just remember to keep your fingering the same as in the original **"Scale Pattern."** By learning to start the scales on different frets, allows you to play these scales in different Keys.

"TWELVE BAR CHORD PROGRESSIONS"
TO PLAY ALONG WITH SCALES:

You will find a standard **"Twelve Bar Chord Progression"** that can be used as an accompaniment for the **Major Pentatonic, Minor Pentatonic** and **"Blues Scale."** The chord progression is written in the Key of "A," but you can play it in a different Key once you learn to "move" the scale and transpose the chords to another key. Once you achieve proficiency executing the scales, try recording yourself on tape so you can play the twelve bar chord progression along with the scales. Conversely, try recording the twelve bar chord progression and play the scales "over the chords." Even better, get a friend to play the chords while you execute the scales. Most of all, have fun.

Part I

MAJOR SCALES

(Eight Note, Single Octave Scales)

"A" Major Scale
Pattern 6-I

"SCALE PATH"

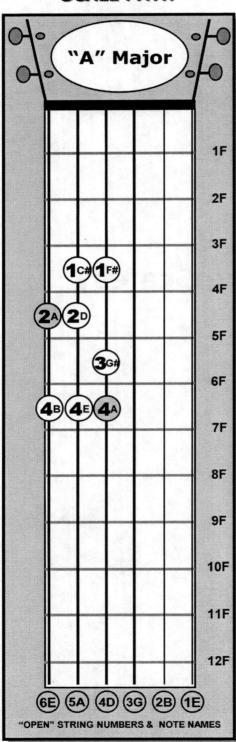

"HOW TO USE THE ILLUSTRATIONS"

THE SCALE PATH: MATCH THE NUMBERED FINGERS IN THE HAND ILLUSTRATION AT THE BOTTOM OF THIS PAGE WITH THE CIRCLED NUMBERS ON THE SCALE PATH FOR CORRECT FINGERING.

TABLATURE: MATCH THE NUMBERED FINGERS IN THE HAND ILLUSTRATION AT THE BOTTOM OF THIS PAGE WITH THE NUMBER(S) IN THE OVAL SHAPED CIRCLES IN THE TABLATURE.

FRET NUMBER   FINGER NUMBER

THE FAR LEFT SIDE OF THE **TABLATURE** LISTS THE **OPEN** STRING NUMBERS AND CORRESPONDING NOTE NAMES:

EXAMPLE: (1E-2B-3G-4D-5A-6E)

THE SCALE PATTERNS ARE MOVEABLE: REMEMBER THAT ALL THE SCALE PATTERNS IN THIS BOOK ARE MOVEABLE. THAT IS TO SAY THEY CAN BE PLAYED BY STARTING ON ANY FRET, SO LONG AS ONLY FRETTED NOTES ARE INCLUDED IN THE SCALE (NO OPEN NOTES). SEE THE **"MOVEABLE SCALE PATTERN"** DIRECTLY BELOW THE **"TABLATURE"** SECTION FOR TWO ADDITIONAL SCALES USING THIS PATTERN.

NUMBER 1 (INDEX FINGER)
NUMBER 2 (MIDDLE FINGER)
NUMBER 3 (RING FINGER)
NUMBER 4 (PINKY FINGER)

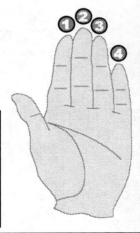

SEE OUR **"SCALE FINDER"**
ON PAGE 54 FOR ALL SCALES THAT
ARE BASED ON THIS PATTERN.
REMEMBER, THE FIRST NUMBER IN THE
SCALE **PATTERN NAME** MEANS THAT THE
PATTERN STARTS ON THAT
NUMBERED STRING **ONLY!**

"A" Major Scale

Pattern 6-I Standard Notation & Tablature

"STANDARD NOTATION"

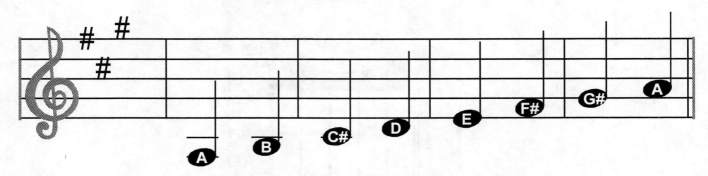

"TABLATURE"

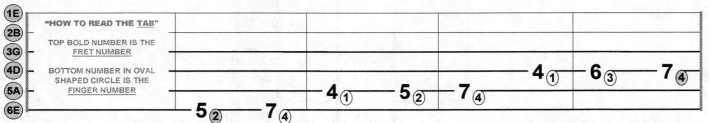

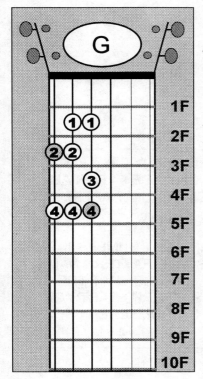

"MOVEABLE SCALE PATTERN"

THE DIAGRAMS TO THE LEFT AND RIGHT SHOW HOW THE SAME **"SCALE PATTERN"** CAN BE MOVED ALONG THE GUITAR NECK SO THAT THE SCALE CAN BE PLAYED IN A NEW POSITION AND KEY.

LEFT - THE **"SCALE PATTERN"** HAS BEEN MOVED DOWN THE NECK TWO (2) FRETS (LOWER IN PITCH).

RIGHT - THE **"SCALE PATTERN"** HAS BEEN MOVED UP THE NECK ONE (1) FRET (HIGHER IN PITCH).

(SEE PAGE 26 FOR MORE DETAIL)

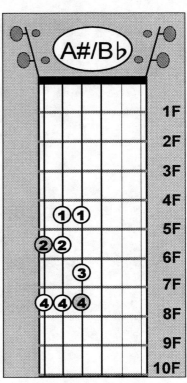

"A" Major Scale
Pattern 6-II

"SCALE PATH"

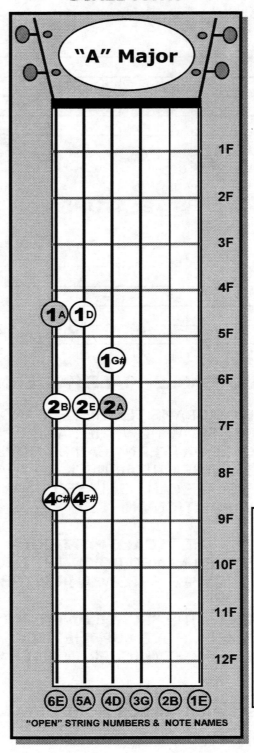

"A" Major

1F
2F
3F
4F
5F
6F
7F
8F
9F
10F
11F
12F

6E 5A 4D 3G 2B 1E

"OPEN" STRING NUMBERS & NOTE NAMES

SEE OUR **"SCALE FINDER"** ON PAGE 54 FOR ALL SCALES THAT ARE BASED ON THIS PATTERN. REMEMBER, THE FIRST NUMBER IN THE SCALE **PATTERN NAME** MEANS THAT THE PATTERN STARTS ON THAT NUMBERED STRING **ONLY!**

"A" Major Scale

Pattern 6-II Standard Notation & Tablature

"STANDARD NOTATION"

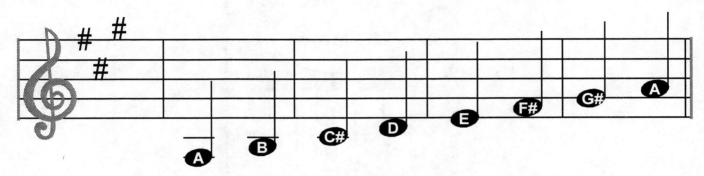

"TABLATURE"

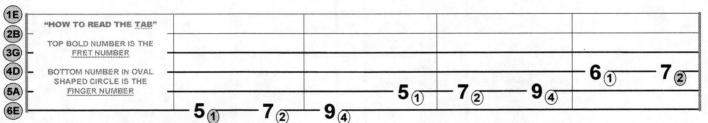

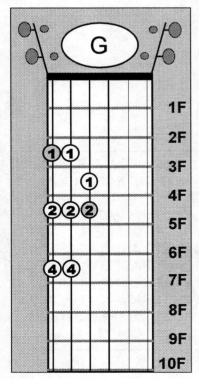

"MOVEABLE SCALE PATTERN"

THE DIAGRAMS TO THE LEFT AND RIGHT SHOW HOW THE SAME **"SCALE PATTERN"** CAN BE MOVED ALONG THE GUITAR NECK SO THAT THE SCALE CAN BE PLAYED IN A NEW POSITION AND KEY.

LEFT - THE **"SCALE PATTERN"** HAS BEEN MOVED DOWN THE NECK TWO (2) FRETS (LOWER IN PITCH).

RIGHT - THE **"SCALE PATTERN"** HAS BEEN MOVED UP THE NECK ONE (1) FRET (HIGHER IN PITCH).

(SEE PAGE 26 FOR MORE DETAIL)

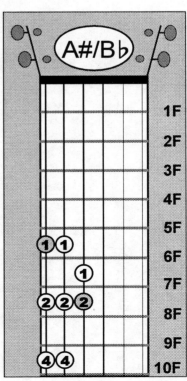

"A" Major Scale
Pattern 6-III

"SCALE PATH"

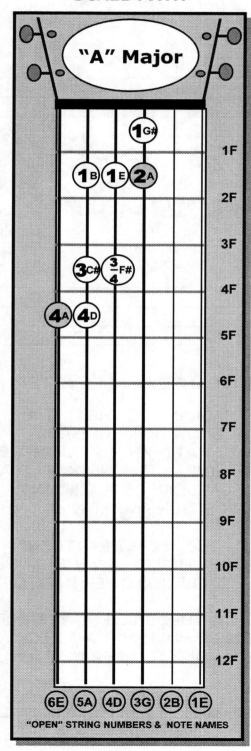

SEE OUR **"SCALE FINDER"** ON PAGE 54 FOR ALL SCALES THAT ARE BASED ON THIS PATTERN. REMEMBER, THE FIRST NUMBER IN THE SCALE **PATTERN NAME** MEANS THAT THE PATTERN STARTS ON THAT NUMBERED STRING **ONLY!**

"A" Major Scale

Pattern 6-III Standard Notation & Tablature

"STANDARD NOTATION"

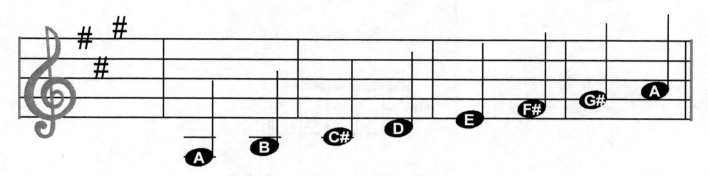

"TABLATURE"

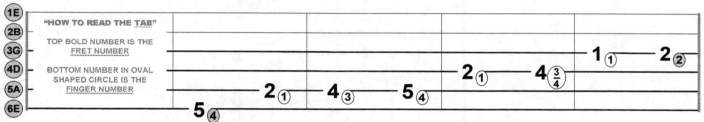

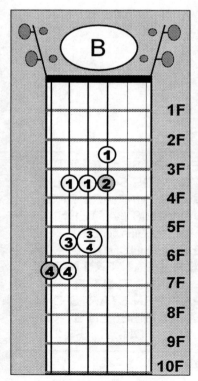

"MOVEABLE SCALE PATTERN"

THE DIAGRAMS TO THE LEFT AND RIGHT SHOW HOW THE SAME "SCALE PATTERN" CAN BE MOVED ALONG THE GUITAR NECK SO THAT THE SCALE CAN BE PLAYED IN A NEW POSITION AND KEY.

LEFT - THE **"SCALE PATTERN"** HAS BEEN MOVED UP THE NECK TWO (2) FRETS (HIGHER IN PITCH).

RIGHT - THE **"SCALE PATTERN"** HAS BEEN MOVED UP THE NECK FIVE (5) FRETS (HIGHER IN PITCH).

(SEE PAGE 26 FOR MORE DETAIL)

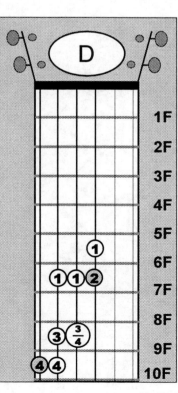

"D" Major Scale
Pattern 5-I

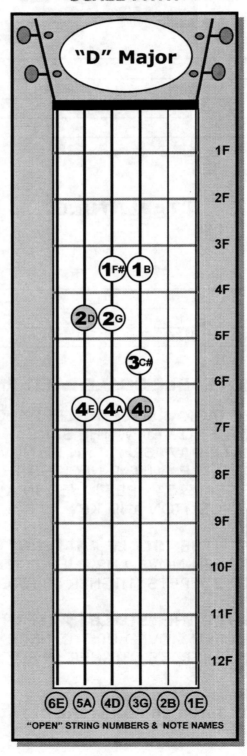

"SCALE PATH"

"D" Major

1F
2F
3F
1F# **1**B
4F
2D **2**G
5F
3C#
6F
4E **4**A **4**D
7F
8F
9F
10F
11F
12F

⑥E ⑤A ④D ③G ②B ①E

"OPEN" STRING NUMBERS & NOTE NAMES

SEE OUR **"SCALE FINDER"**
ON PAGE 54 FOR ALL
SCALES THAT ARE BASED
ON THIS PATTERN.
REMEMBER,
THE FIRST NUMBER IN THE
SCALE **PATTERN NAME**
MEANS THAT THE
PATTERN STARTS ON
THAT NUMBERED STRING
ONLY!

"D" Major Scale

Pattern 5-I Standard Notation & Tablature

"STANDARD NOTATION"

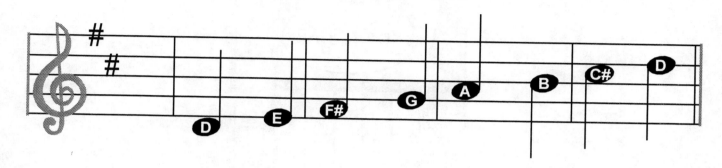

"TABLATURE"

1E	
2B	
3G	
4D	
5A	
6E	

"HOW TO READ THE TAB"

TOP BOLD NUMBER IS THE FRET NUMBER

BOTTOM NUMBER IN OVAL SHAPED CIRCLE IS THE FINGER NUMBER

5② 7④ 4① 5② 7④ 4① 6③ 7④

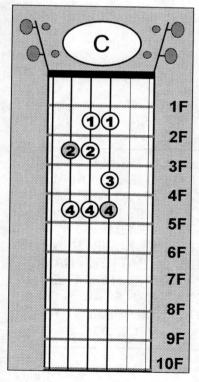

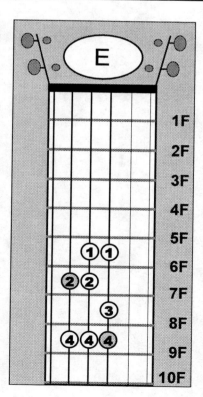

"MOVEABLE SCALE PATTERN"

THE DIAGRAMS TO THE LEFT AND RIGHT SHOW HOW THE SAME **"SCALE PATTERN"** CAN BE MOVED ALONG THE GUITAR NECK SO THAT THE SCALE CAN BE PLAYED IN A NEW POSITION AND KEY.

LEFT - THE **"SCALE PATTERN"** HAS BEEN MOVED DOWN THE NECK TWO (2) FRETS (LOWER IN PITCH).

RIGHT - THE **"SCALE PATTERN"** HAS BEEN MOVED UP THE NECK TWO (2) FRETS (HIGHER IN PITCH).

(SEE PAGE 26 FOR MORE DETAIL)

"D" Major Scale
Pattern 5-II

"SCALE PATH"

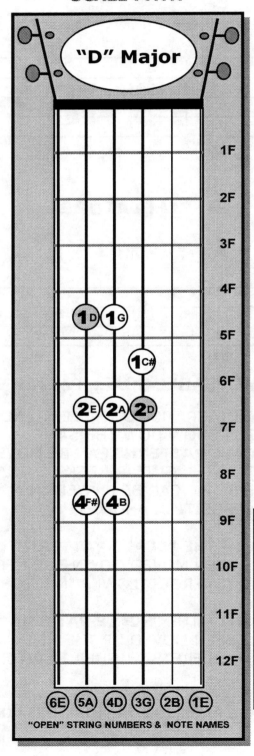

"OPEN" STRING NUMBERS & NOTE NAMES

SEE OUR **"SCALE FINDER"** ON PAGE 54 FOR ALL SCALES THAT ARE BASED ON THIS PATTERN. REMEMBER, THE FIRST NUMBER IN THE SCALE **PATTERN NAME** MEANS THAT THE PATTERN STARTS ON THAT NUMBERED STRING **ONLY!**

"D" Major Scale

Pattern 5-II Standard Notation & Tablature

"STANDARD NOTATION"

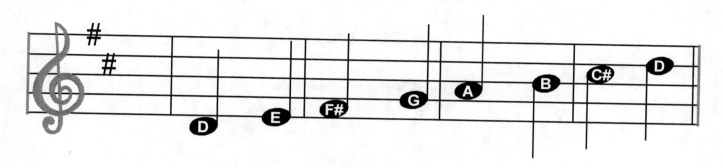

"TABLATURE"

1E	
2B	
3G	
4D	
5A	
6E	

"HOW TO READ THE TAB"

TOP BOLD NUMBER IS THE FRET NUMBER

BOTTOM NUMBER IN OVAL SHAPED CIRCLE IS THE FINGER NUMBER

5① — 7② — 9④ 5① — 7② — 9④ 6① — 7②

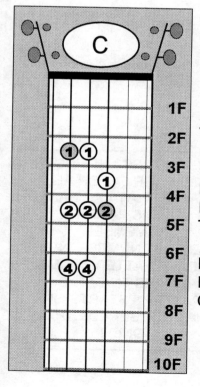

"MOVEABLE SCALE PATTERN"

THE DIAGRAMS TO THE LEFT AND RIGHT SHOW HOW THE SAME **"SCALE PATTERN"** CAN BE MOVED ALONG THE GUITAR NECK SO THAT THE SCALE CAN BE PLAYED IN A NEW POSITION AND KEY.

LEFT - THE **"SCALE PATTERN"** HAS BEEN MOVED DOWN THE NECK TWO (2) FRETS (LOWER IN PITCH).

RIGHT - THE **"SCALE PATTERN"** HAS BEEN MOVED UP THE NECK ONE (1) FRET (HIGHER IN PITCH).

(SEE PAGE 26 FOR MORE DETAIL)

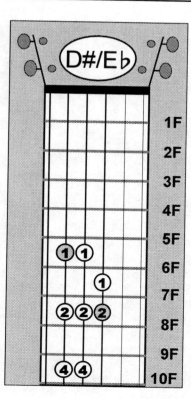

"D" Major Scale
Pattern 5-III

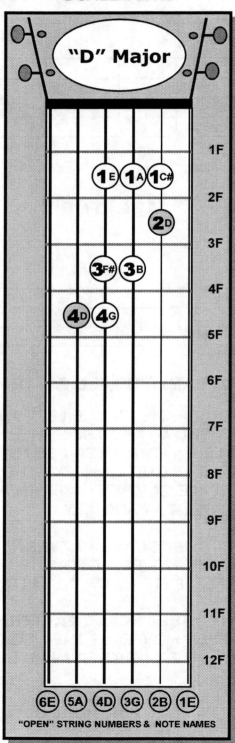

"SCALE PATH"

"D" Major

1F

1E 1A 1C#

2F

2D

3F

3F# 3B

4F

4D 4G

5F

6F

7F

8F

9F

10F

11F

12F

6E 5A 4D 3G 2B 1E

"OPEN" STRING NUMBERS & NOTE NAMES

SEE OUR **"SCALE FINDER"** ON PAGE 54 FOR ALL SCALES THAT ARE BASED ON THIS PATTERN. REMEMBER, THE FIRST NUMBER IN THE SCALE **PATTERN NAME** MEANS THAT THE PATTERN STARTS ON THAT NUMBERED STRING **ONLY!**

"D" Major Scale
Pattern 5-III Standard Notation & Tablature

"STANDARD NOTATION"

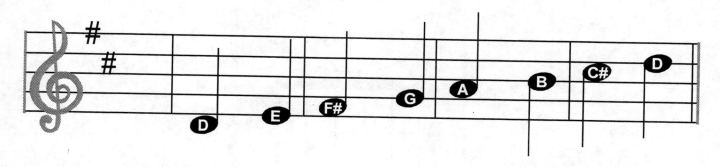

"TABLATURE"

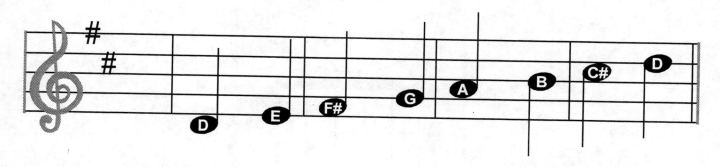

"HOW TO READ THE TAB"

TOP BOLD NUMBER IS THE FRET NUMBER

BOTTOM NUMBER IN OVAL SHAPED CIRCLE IS THE FINGER NUMBER

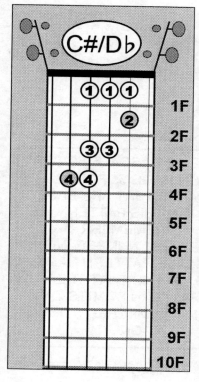

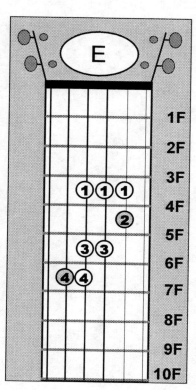

"MOVEABLE SCALE PATTERN"

THE DIAGRAMS TO THE LEFT AND RIGHT SHOW HOW THE SAME "SCALE PATTERN" CAN BE MOVED ALONG THE GUITAR NECK SO THAT THE SCALE CAN BE PLAYED IN A NEW POSITION AND KEY.

LEFT - THE "SCALE PATTERN" HAS BEEN MOVED DOWN THE NECK ONE (1) FRET (LOWER IN PITCH).

RIGHT - THE "SCALE PATTERN" HAS BEEN MOVED UP THE NECK TWO (2) FRETS (HIGHER IN PITCH).

(SEE PAGE 26 FOR MORE DETAIL)

39

"G" Major Scale
Pattern 4-I

"SCALE PATH"

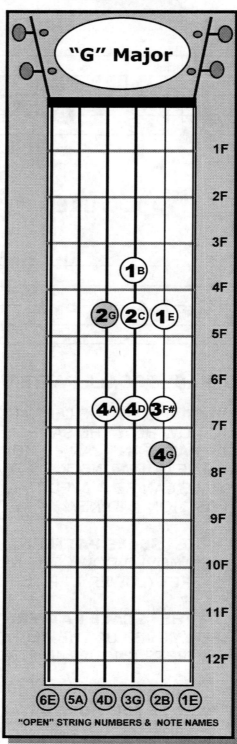

"G" Major

1F
2F
3F
4F
5F
6F
7F
8F
9F
10F
11F
12F

1B
2G 2C 1E
4A 4D 3F#
4G

6E 5A 4D 3G 2B 1E

"OPEN" STRING NUMBERS & NOTE NAMES

SEE OUR **"SCALE FINDER"** ON PAGE 55 FOR ALL SCALES THAT ARE BASED ON THIS PATTERN. REMEMBER, THE FIRST NUMBER IN THE SCALE **PATTERN NAME** MEANS THAT THE PATTERN STARTS ON THAT NUMBERED STRING **ONLY!**

"G" Major Scale
Pattern 4-I Standard Notation & Tablature

"STANDARD NOTATION"

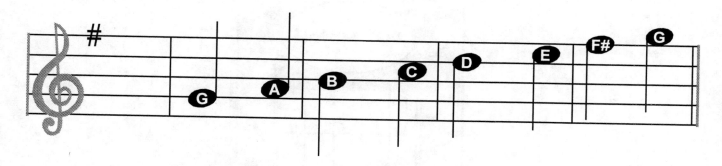

"TABLATURE"

"HOW TO READ THE TAB"

TOP BOLD NUMBER IS THE FRET NUMBER

BOTTOM NUMBER IN OVAL SHAPED CIRCLE IS THE FINGER NUMBER

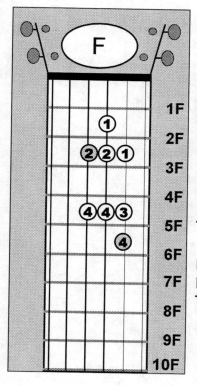

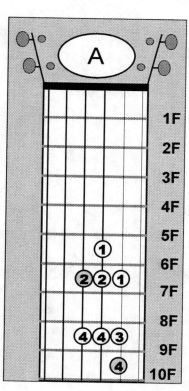

"MOVEABLE SCALE PATTERN"

THE DIAGRAMS TO THE LEFT AND RIGHT SHOW HOW THE SAME **"SCALE PATTERN"** CAN BE MOVED ALONG THE GUITAR NECK SO THAT THE SCALE CAN BE PLAYED IN A NEW POSITION AND KEY.

LEFT - THE **"SCALE PATTERN"** HAS BEEN MOVED DOWN THE NECK TWO (2) FRETS (LOWER IN PITCH).

RIGHT - THE **"SCALE PATTERN"** HAS BEEN MOVED UP THE NECK TWO (2) FRETS (HIGHER IN PITCH).

(SEE PAGE 26 FOR MORE DETAIL)

"G" Major Scale
(Optional Fingering)
Pattern 4-I

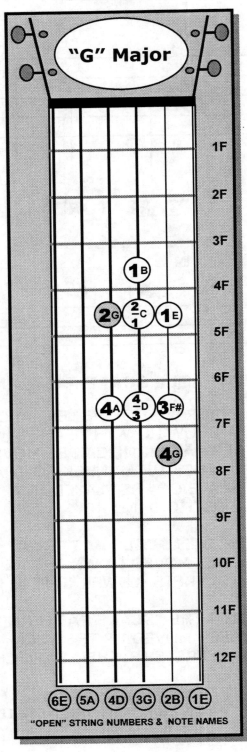

"SCALE PATH"

"G" Major

1F
2F
3F
4F — 1B
5F — 2G 2/1 C 1E
6F
7F — 4A 4/3 D 3F#
8F — 4G
9F
10F
11F
12F

6E 5A 4D 3G 2B 1E

"OPEN" STRING NUMBERS & NOTE NAMES

"G" Major Scale
(Optional Fingering)
Pattern 4-I Standard Notation & Tablature

"STANDARD NOTATION"

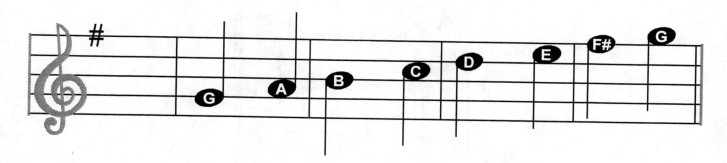

"TABLATURE"

"HOW TO READ THE TAB"

TOP BOLD NUMBER IS THE FRET NUMBER

BOTTOM NUMBER IN OVAL SHAPED CIRCLE IS THE FINGER NUMBER

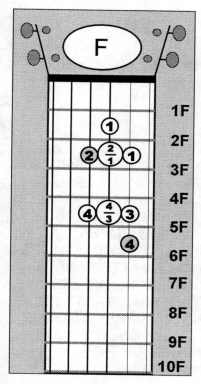

"MOVEABLE SCALE PATTERN"

THE DIAGRAMS TO THE LEFT AND RIGHT SHOW HOW THE SAME "SCALE PATTERN" CAN BE MOVED ALONG THE GUITAR NECK SO THAT THE SCALE CAN BE PLAYED IN A NEW POSITION AND KEY.

LEFT - THE "SCALE PATTERN" HAS BEEN MOVED DOWN THE NECK TWO (2) FRETS (LOWER IN PITCH).

RIGHT - THE "SCALE PATTERN" HAS BEEN MOVED UP THE NECK TWO (2) FRETS (HIGHER IN PITCH).

(SEE PAGE 26 FOR MORE DETAIL)

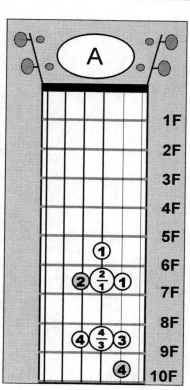

"G" Major Scale
Pattern 4-II

"SCALE PATH"

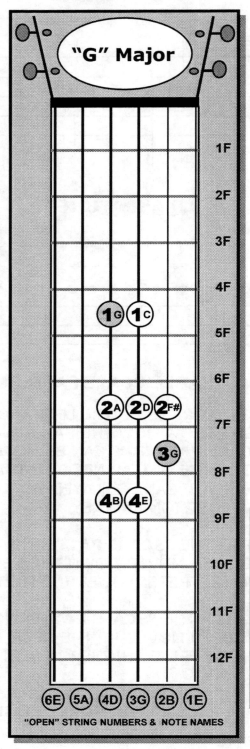

"G" Major

1F
2F
3F
4F
5F
6F
7F
8F
9F
10F
11F
12F

⑥E ⑤A ④D ③G ②B ①E

"OPEN" STRING NUMBERS & NOTE NAMES

SEE OUR **"SCALE FINDER"** ON PAGE 55 FOR ALL SCALES THAT ARE BASED ON THIS PATTERN. REMEMBER, THE FIRST NUMBER IN THE SCALE **PATTERN NAME** MEANS THAT THE PATTERN STARTS ON THAT NUMBERED STRING **ONLY!**

"G" Major Scale
Pattern 4-II Standard Notation & Tablature

"STANDARD NOTATION"

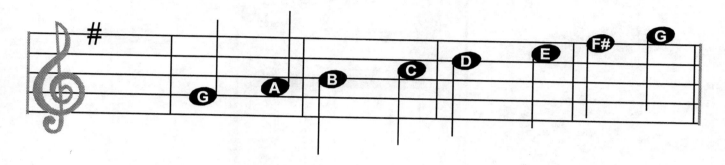

"TABLATURE"

"HOW TO READ THE TAB"

TOP BOLD NUMBER IS THE FRET NUMBER

BOTTOM NUMBER IN OVAL SHAPED CIRCLE IS THE FINGER NUMBER

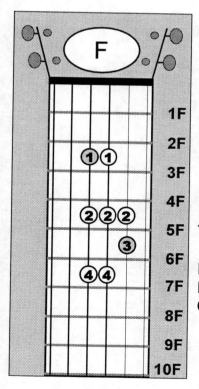

"MOVEABLE SCALE PATTERN"

THE DIAGRAMS TO THE LEFT AND RIGHT SHOW HOW THE SAME **"SCALE PATTERN"** CAN BE MOVED ALONG THE GUITAR NECK SO THAT THE SCALE CAN BE PLAYED IN A NEW POSITION AND KEY.

LEFT - THE **"SCALE PATTERN"** HAS BEEN MOVED DOWN THE NECK TWO (2) FRETS (LOWER IN PITCH).

RIGHT - THE **"SCALE PATTERN"** HAS BEEN MOVED UP THE NECK ONE (1) FRET (HIGHER IN PITCH).

(SEE PAGE 26 FOR MORE DETAIL)

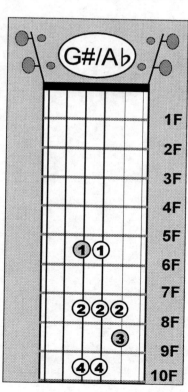

"G" Major Scale
(Optional Fingering)
Pattern 4-II

"SCALE PATH"

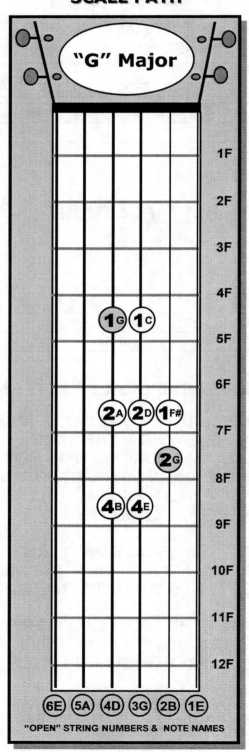

46

"G" Major Scale
(Optional Fingering)
Pattern 4-II Standard Notation & Tablature

"STANDARD NOTATION"

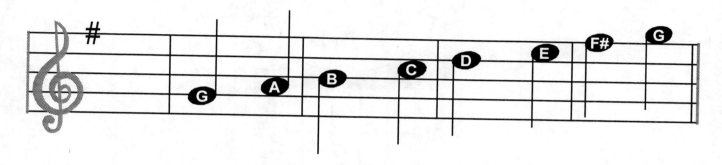

"TABLATURE"

1E					
2B					
3G	"HOW TO READ THE TAB"				7① 8②
4D	TOP BOLD NUMBER IS THE FRET NUMBER		5① 7②	9④	
5A	BOTTOM NUMBER IN OVAL SHAPED CIRCLE IS THE FINGER NUMBER	5① 7②	9④		
6E					

"MOVEABLE SCALE PATTERN"

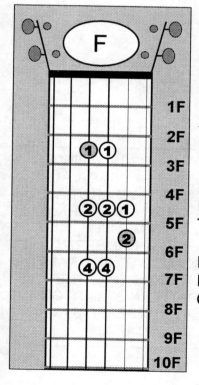

THE DIAGRAMS TO THE LEFT AND RIGHT SHOW HOW THE SAME **"SCALE PATTERN"** CAN BE MOVED ALONG THE GUITAR NECK SO THAT THE SCALE CAN BE PLAYED IN A NEW POSITION AND KEY.

LEFT - THE **"SCALE PATTERN"** HAS BEEN MOVED DOWN THE NECK TWO (2) FRETS (LOWER IN PITCH).

RIGHT - THE **"SCALE PATTERN"** HAS BEEN MOVED UP THE NECK ONE (1) FRET (HIGHER IN PITCH).

(SEE PAGE 26 FOR MORE DETAIL)

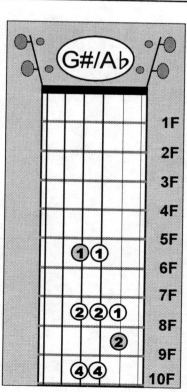

"G" Major Scale
Pattern 4-III

"SCALE PATH"

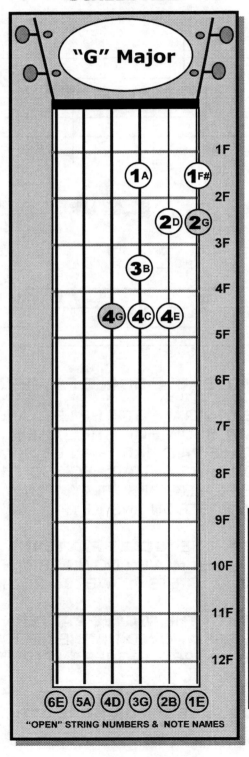

SEE OUR **"SCALE FINDER"** ON PAGE 55 FOR ALL SCALES THAT ARE BASED ON THIS PATTERN. REMEMBER, THE FIRST NUMBER IN THE SCALE **PATTERN NAME** MEANS THAT THE PATTERN STARTS ON THAT NUMBERED STRING **ONLY!**

"G" Major Scale
Pattern 4-III Standard Notation & Tablature

"STANDARD NOTATION"

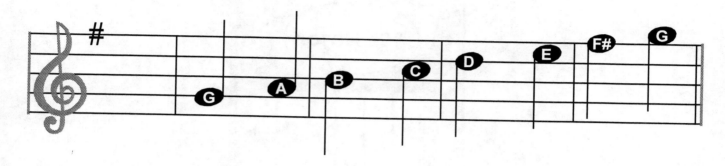

"TABLATURE"

"HOW TO READ THE TAB"

TOP BOLD NUMBER IS THE FRET NUMBER

BOTTOM NUMBER IN OVAL SHAPED CIRCLE IS THE FINGER NUMBER

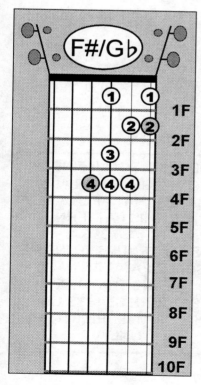

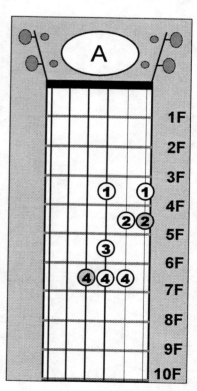

"MOVEABLE SCALE PATTERN"

THE DIAGRAMS TO THE LEFT AND RIGHT SHOW HOW THE SAME "SCALE PATTERN" CAN BE MOVED ALONG THE GUITAR NECK SO THAT THE SCALE CAN BE PLAYED IN A NEW POSITION AND KEY.

LEFT - THE "SCALE PATTERN" HAS BEEN MOVED DOWN THE NECK ONE (1) FRETS (LOWER IN PITCH).

RIGHT - THE "SCALE PATTERN" HAS BEEN MOVED UP THE NECK TWO (2) FRETS (HIGHER IN PITCH).

(SEE PAGE 26 FOR MORE DETAIL)

"C" Major Scale
Pattern 3-I

"SCALE PATH"

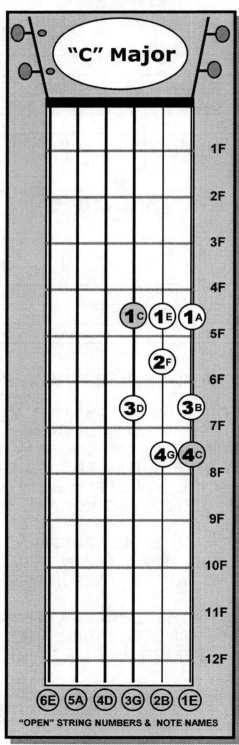

"C" Major

1F
2F
3F
4F

①c ①E ①A
5F

②F
6F

③D ③B
7F

④G ④C
8F

9F
10F
11F
12F

⑥E ⑤A ④D ③G ②B ①E

"OPEN" STRING NUMBERS & NOTE NAMES

SEE OUR **"SCALE FINDER"** ON PAGE 55 FOR ALL SCALES THAT ARE BASED ON THIS PATTERN. REMEMBER, THE FIRST NUMBER IN THE SCALE **PATTERN NAME** MEANS THAT THE PATTERN STARTS ON THAT NUMBERED STRING **ONLY!**

"C" Major Scale
Pattern 3-I Standard Notation & Tablature

"STANDARD NOTATION"

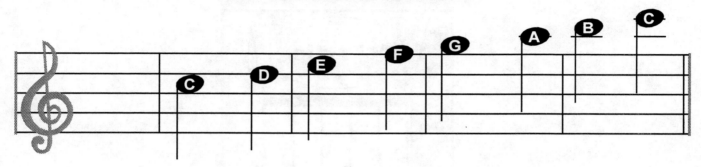

"TABLATURE"

1E	
2B	"HOW TO READ THE TAB"
3G	TOP BOLD NUMBER IS THE FRET NUMBER
4D	BOTTOM NUMBER IN OVAL SHAPED CIRCLE IS THE FINGER NUMBER
5A	
6E	

"MOVEABLE SCALE PATTERN"

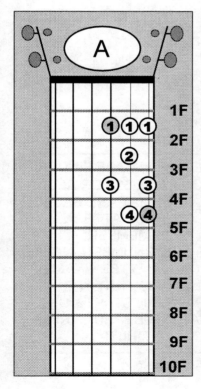

THE DIAGRAMS TO THE LEFT AND RIGHT SHOW HOW THE SAME **"SCALE PATTERN"** CAN BE MOVED ALONG THE GUITAR NECK SO THAT THE SCALE CAN BE PLAYED IN A NEW POSITION AND KEY.

LEFT - THE **"SCALE PATTERN"** HAS BEEN MOVED DOWN THE NECK THREE (3) FRETS (LOWER IN PITCH).

RIGHT - THE **"SCALE PATTERN"** HAS BEEN MOVED UP THE NECK TWO (2) FRETS (HIGHER IN PITCH).

(SEE PAGE 26 FOR MORE DETAIL)

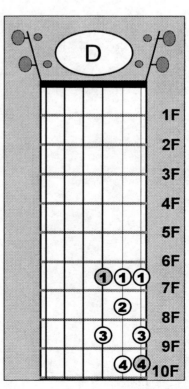

"C" Major Scale
Pattern 3-II

"SCALE PATH"

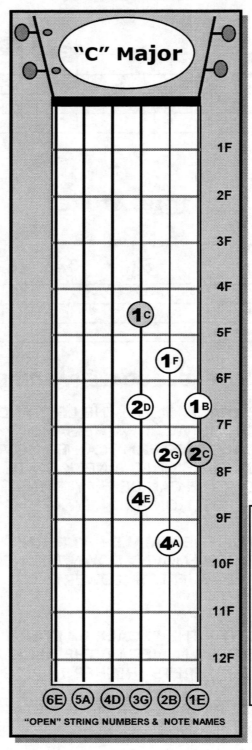

"C" Major

1F
2F
3F
4F

1C

5F

1F

6F

2D   **1**B

7F

2G **2**C

8F

4E

9F

4A

10F
11F
12F

6E 5A 4D 3G 2B 1E

"OPEN" STRING NUMBERS & NOTE NAMES

SEE OUR **"SCALE FINDER"** ON PAGE 55 FOR ALL SCALES THAT ARE BASED ON THIS PATTERN. REMEMBER, THE FIRST NUMBER IN THE SCALE **PATTERN NAME** MEANS THAT THE PATTERN STARTS ON THAT NUMBERED STRING **ONLY!**

"C" Major Scale

Pattern 3-II Standard Notation & Tablature

"STANDARD NOTATION"

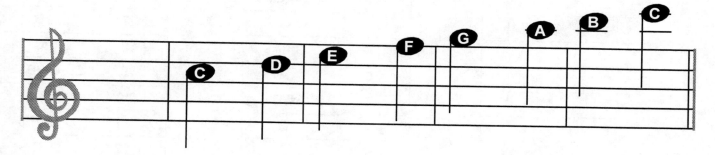

"TABLATURE"

1E	
2B	
3G	
4D	
5A	
6E	

"HOW TO READ THE TAB"

TOP BOLD NUMBER IS THE FRET NUMBER

BOTTOM NUMBER IN OVAL SHAPED CIRCLE IS THE FINGER NUMBER

5 ① 7 ② 9 ④ 6 ① 8 ② 10 ④ 7 ① 8 ②

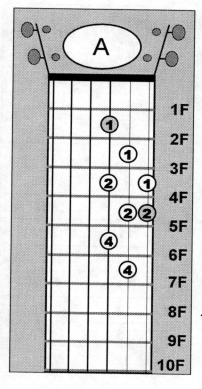

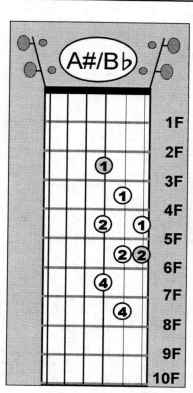

"MOVEABLE SCALE PATTERN"

THE DIAGRAMS TO THE LEFT AND RIGHT SHOW HOW THE SAME **"SCALE PATTERN"** CAN BE MOVED ALONG THE GUITAR NECK SO THAT THE SCALE CAN BE PLAYED IN A NEW POSITION AND KEY.

LEFT - THE **"SCALE PATTERN"** HAS BEEN MOVED DOWN THE NECK THREE (3) FRETS (LOWER IN PITCH).

RIGHT - THE **"SCALE PATTERN"** HAS BEEN MOVED DOWN THE NECK TWO (2) FRETS (LOWER IN PITCH).

(SEE PAGE 26 FOR MORE DETAIL)

SCALE FINDER

<table>
<tr><td rowspan="2">THIS PATTERN IS ON PAGE 28</td><td colspan="2">PATTERN 6-I</td></tr>
<tr><td>*Starting Fret</td><td>Scale Name</td></tr>
<tr><td></td><td>2</td><td>F#/G♭</td></tr>
<tr><td></td><td>3</td><td>G</td></tr>
<tr><td></td><td>4</td><td>G#/A♭</td></tr>
<tr><td></td><td>5</td><td>A</td></tr>
<tr><td></td><td>6</td><td>A#/B♭</td></tr>
<tr><td></td><td>7</td><td>B</td></tr>
<tr><td></td><td>8</td><td>C</td></tr>
<tr><td></td><td>9</td><td>C#/D♭</td></tr>
<tr><td></td><td>10</td><td>D</td></tr>
<tr><td></td><td>11</td><td>D#/E♭</td></tr>
<tr><td></td><td>12</td><td>E</td></tr>
<tr><td></td><td>13</td><td>F</td></tr>
</table>

THIS PATTERN IS ON PAGE 30	PATTERN 6-II	
	*Starting Fret	Scale Name
	1	F
	2	F#/G♭
	3	G
	4	G#/A♭
	5	A
	6	A#/B♭
	7	B
	8	C
	9	C#/D♭
	10	D
	11	D#/E♭
	12	E

THIS PATTERN IS ON PAGE 32	PATTERN 6-III	
	*Starting Fret	Scale Name
	5	A
	6	A#/B♭
	7	B
	8	C
	9	C#/D♭
	10	D
	11	D#/E♭
	12	E
	13	F

*The "Starting Fret" = Circled "Root" Note In The "Scale Path" Diagram

THIS PATTERN IS ON PAGE 34	PATTERN 5-I	
	*Starting Fret	Scale Name
	2	B
	3	C
	4	C#/D♭
	5	D
	6	D#/E♭
	7	E
	8	F
	9	F#/G♭
	10	G
	11	G#/A♭
	12	A
	13	A#/B♭

THIS PATTERN IS ON PAGE 36	PATTERN 5-II	
	*Starting Fret	Scale Name
	1	B♭
	2	B
	3	C
	4	C#/D♭
	5	D
	6	D#/E♭
	7	E
	8	F
	9	F#/G♭
	10	G
	11	G#/A♭
	12	A

THIS PATTERN IS ON PAGE 38	PATTERN 5-III	
	*Starting Fret	Scale Name
	4	C#/D♭
	5	D
	6	D#/E♭
	7	E
	8	F
	9	F#/G♭
	10	G
	11	G#/A♭
	12	A
	13	A#/B♭
	14	B
	15	C

SCALE FINDER

THIS PATTERN IS ON PAGE 40

PATTERN 4-I

*Starting Fret	Scale Name
2	E
3	F
4	F#/G♭
5	G
6	G#/A♭
7	A
8	A#/B♭
9	B
10	C
11	C#/D♭
12	D
13	D#/E♭

THIS PATTERN IS ON PAGE 44

PATTERN 4-II

*Starting Fret	Scale Name
1	D#/E♭
2	E
3	F
4	F#/G♭
5	G
6	G#/A♭
7	A
8	A#/B♭
9	B
10	C
11	C#/D♭
12	D
13	D#/E♭

THIS PATTERN IS ON PAGE 48

PATTERN 4-III

*Starting Fret	Scale Name
4	F#/G♭
5	G
6	G#/A♭
7	A
8	A#/B♭
9	B
10	C
11	C#/D♭
12	D
13	D#/E♭
14	E
15	F

THIS PATTERN IS ON PAGE 50

PATTERN 3-I

*Starting Fret	Scale Name
1	G#/A♭
2	A
3	A#/B♭
4	B
5	C
6	C#/D♭
7	D
8	D#/E♭
9	E
10	F
11	F#/G♭
12	G
13	G#/A♭

THIS PATTERN IS ON PAGE 52

PATTERN 3-II

*Starting Fret	Scale Name
1	G#/A♭
2	A
3	A#/B♭
4	B
5	C
6	C#/D♭
7	D
8	D#/E♭
9	E
10	F
11	F#/G♭
12	G

PRACTICE & PATIENCE ARE THE KEYS
TO SUCCESSFULLY LEARNING TO PLAY THE GUITAR

Part II

Combined Major Scales

(Sixteen Note, Double Octave Scales)

"G" Major Scale
(Double Octave Scales)
Pattern 6-I & Pattern 4-III

"SCALE PATH"

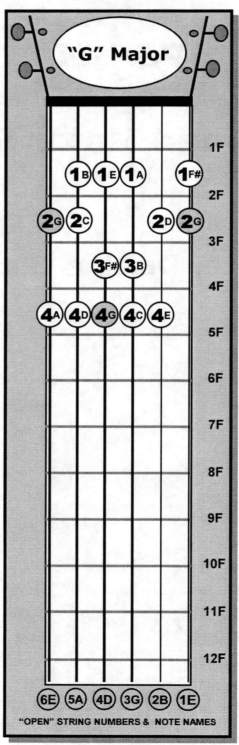

NOTE

WE ARE GOING TO USE PATTERN 6-I THAT WE PREVIOUSLY LEARNED TO PLAY ON PAGE 28. NOTICE THAT WE START PATTERN 6-I ON THIS PAGE ON THE THIRD (3rd) FRET SO WE CAN PLAY IT AS A "G" SCALE. REMEMBER, THE FINGER PATTERNS NEVER CHANGE – ONLY THE FRETS THAT THE SCALE PATTERNS ARE ON CHANGE.

"G" Major Scale
(Double Octave Scales)
Pattern 6-I & Pattern 4-III Standard Notation & Tablature

"STANDARD NOTATION"

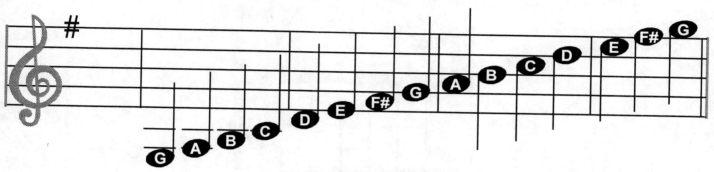

"TABLATURE"

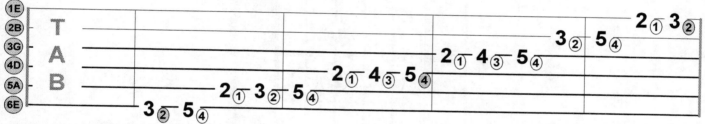

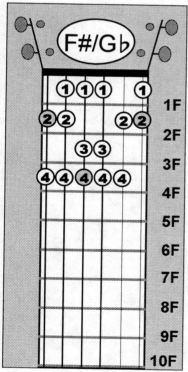

"MOVEABLE SCALE PATTERN"

THE DIAGRAMS TO THE LEFT AND RIGHT SHOW HOW THE SAME "SCALE PATTERN" CAN BE MOVED ALONG THE GUITAR NECK SO THAT THE SCALE CAN BE PLAYED IN A NEW POSITION AND KEY.

LEFT - THE "SCALE PATTERN" HAS BEEN MOVED DOWN THE NECK ONE (1) FRET (LOWER IN PITCH).

RIGHT - THE "SCALE PATTERN" HAS BEEN MOVED UP THE NECK TWO (2) FRETS (HIGHER IN PITCH).

(SEE PAGE 26 FOR MORE DETAIL)

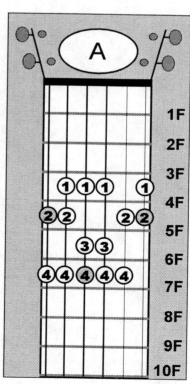

"G" Major Scale
(Double Octave Scales)
Pattern 6-II & Pattern 4-I

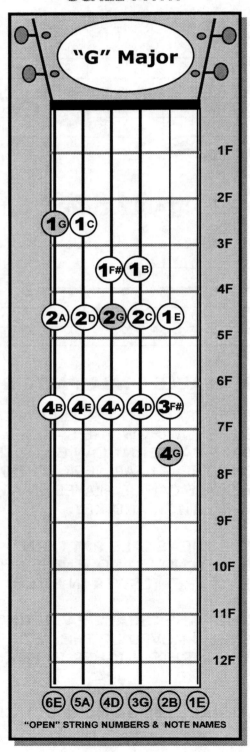

"SCALE PATH"

"OPEN" STRING NUMBERS & NOTE NAMES

"G" Major Scale
(Double Octave Scales)
Pattern 6-II & Pattern 4-I Standard Notation & Tablature

"STANDARD NOTATION"

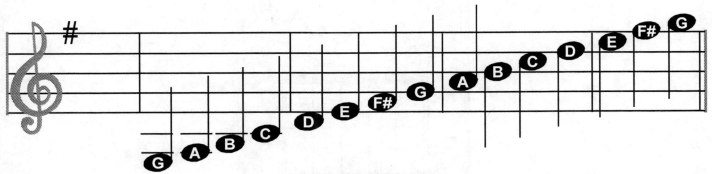

"TABLATURE"

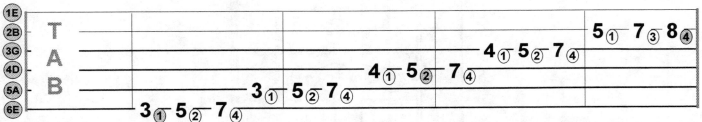

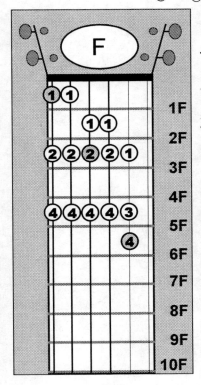

"MOVEABLE SCALE PATTERN"

THE DIAGRAMS TO THE LEFT AND RIGHT SHOW HOW THE SAME "SCALE PATTERN" CAN BE MOVED ALONG THE GUITAR NECK SO THAT THE SCALE CAN BE PLAYED IN A NEW POSITION AND KEY.

LEFT - THE "SCALE PATTERN" HAS BEEN MOVED DOWN THE NECK TWO (2) FRETS (LOWER IN PITCH).

RIGHT - THE "SCALE PATTERN" HAS BEEN MOVED UP THE NECK TWO (2) FRETS (HIGHER IN PITCH).

(SEE PAGE 26 FOR MORE DETAIL)

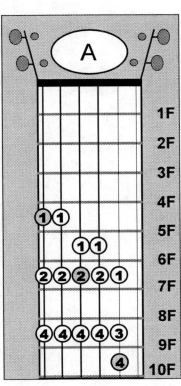

"G" Major Scale (Double Octave Scales)
(Optional Fingering)
Pattern 6-II & Pattern 4-I

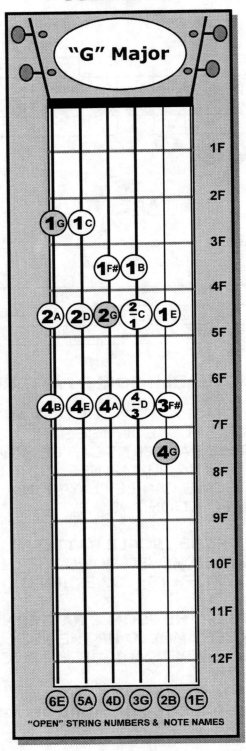

"SCALE PATH"

"G" Major

"G" Major Scale-(Double Octave Scales)
(Optional Fingering)
Pattern 6-II & Pattern 4-I Standard Notation & Tablature

"STANDARD NOTATION"

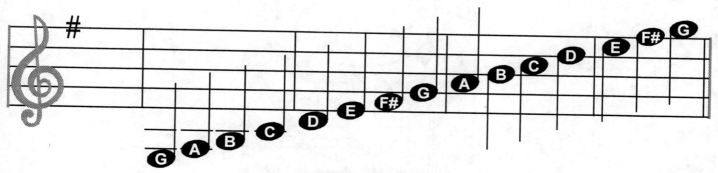

"TABLATURE"

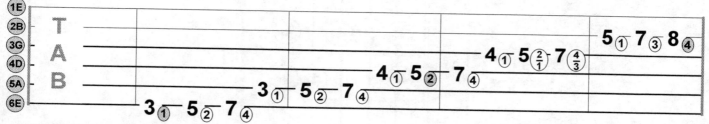

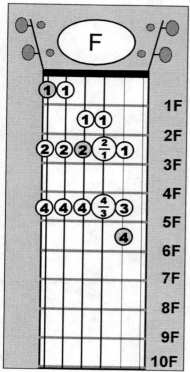

"MOVEABLE SCALE PATTERN"

THE DIAGRAMS TO THE LEFT AND RIGHT SHOW HOW THE SAME **"SCALE PATTERN"** CAN BE MOVED ALONG THE GUITAR NECK SO THAT THE SCALE CAN BE PLAYED IN A NEW POSITION AND KEY.

LEFT - THE **"SCALE PATTERN"** HAS BEEN MOVED DOWN THE NECK TWO (2) FRETS (LOWER IN PITCH).

RIGHT - THE **"SCALE PATTERN"** HAS BEEN MOVED UP THE NECK TWO (2) FRETS (HIGHER IN PITCH).

(SEE PAGE 26 FOR MORE DETAIL)

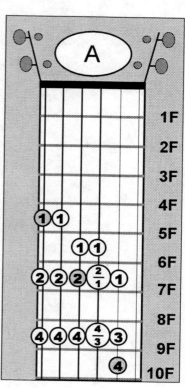

"A" Major Scale
(Double Octave Scales)
Pattern 6-III & Pattern 3-I

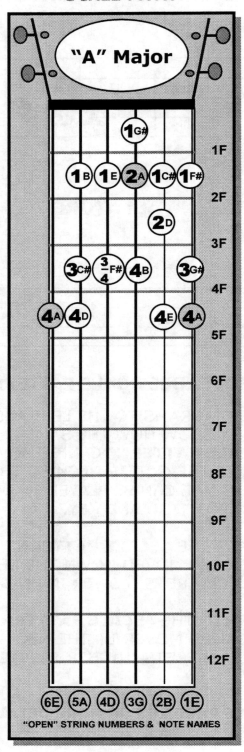

"A" Major Scale
(Double Octave Scales)
Pattern 6-III & Pattern 3-I Standard Notation & Tablature

"STANDARD NOTATION"

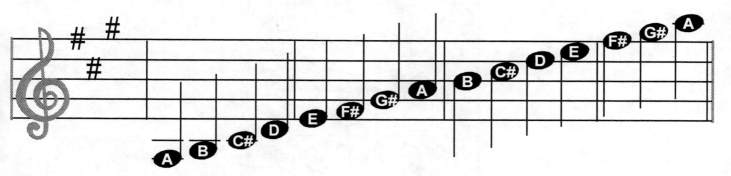

"TABLATURE"

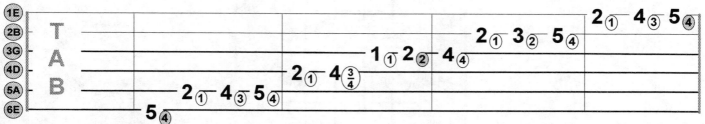

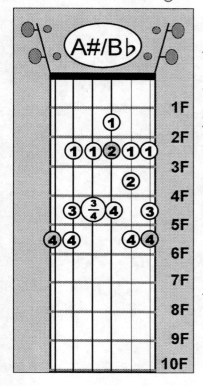

"MOVEABLE SCALE PATTERN"

THE DIAGRAMS TO THE LEFT AND RIGHT SHOW HOW THE SAME **"SCALE PATTERN"** CAN BE MOVED ALONG THE GUITAR NECK SO THAT THE SCALE CAN BE PLAYED IN A NEW POSITION AND KEY.

LEFT - THE **"SCALE PATTERN"** HAS BEEN MOVED UP THE NECK ONE (1) FRET (HIGHER IN PITCH).

RIGHT - THE **"SCALE PATTERN"** HAS BEEN MOVED UP THE NECK THREE (3) FRETS (HIGHER IN PITCH).

(SEE PAGE 26 FOR MORE DETAIL)

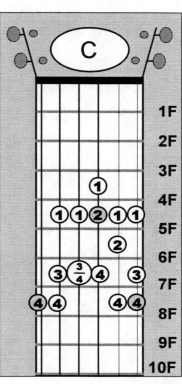

"A" Major Scale (Double Octave Scales)
(Optional Fingering)
Pattern 6-III & Pattern 3-I

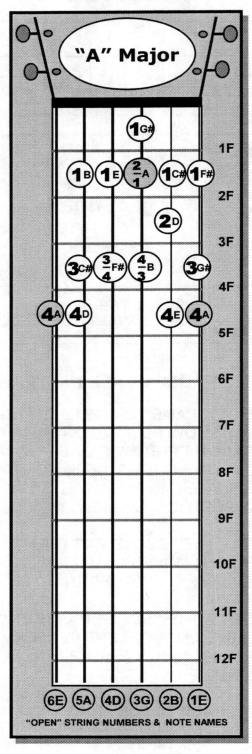

"A" Major Scale (Double Octave Scales)
(Optional Fingering)
Pattern 6-III & Pattern 3-I Standard Notation & Tablature

"STANDARD NOTATION"

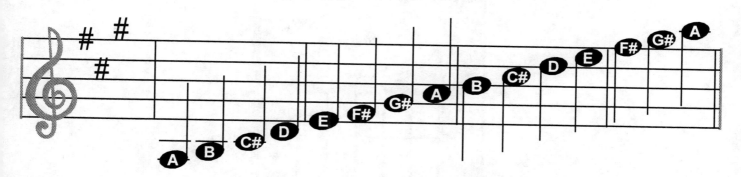

"TABLATURE"

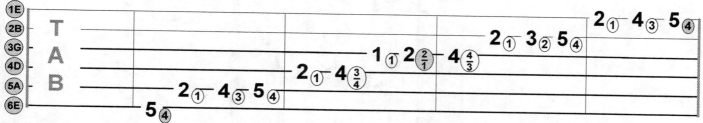

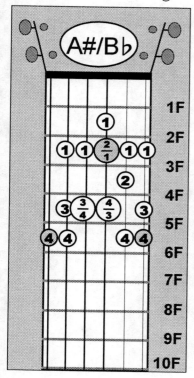

"MOVEABLE SCALE PATTERN"

THE DIAGRAMS TO THE LEFT AND RIGHT SHOW HOW THE SAME "SCALE PATTERN" CAN BE MOVED ALONG THE GUITAR NECK SO THAT THE SCALE CAN BE PLAYED IN A NEW POSITION AND KEY.

LEFT - THE "SCALE PATTERN" HAS BEEN MOVED UP THE NECK ONE (1) FRET (HIGHER IN PITCH).

RIGHT - THE "SCALE PATTERN" HAS BEEN MOVED UP THE NECK THREE (3) FRETS (HIGHER IN PITCH).

(SEE PAGE 26 FOR MORE DETAIL)

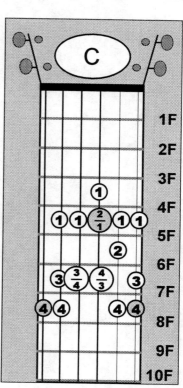

"C" Major Scale
(Double Octave Scales)
Pattern 5-II & Pattern 3-I

"SCALE PATH"

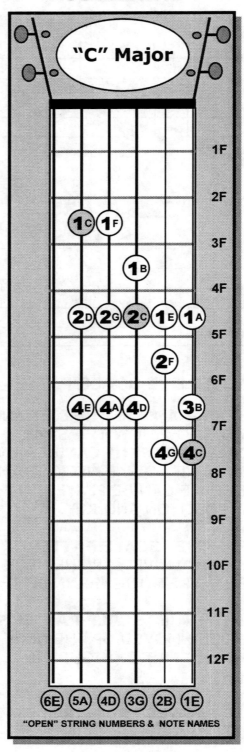

"C" Major Scale
(Double Octave Scales)
Pattern 5-II & Pattern 3-I Standard Notation & Tablature

"STANDARD NOTATION"

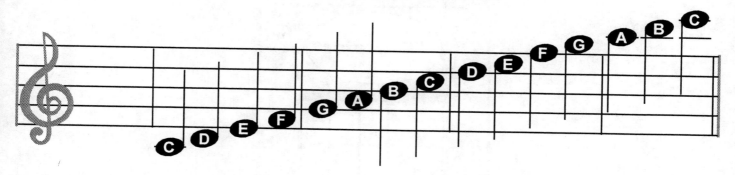

"TABLATURE"

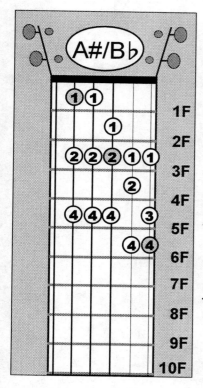

"MOVEABLE SCALE PATTERN"

THE DIAGRAMS TO THE LEFT AND RIGHT SHOW HOW THE SAME **"SCALE PATTERN"** CAN BE MOVED ALONG THE GUITAR NECK SO THAT THE SCALE CAN BE PLAYED IN A NEW POSITION AND KEY.

LEFT - THE **"SCALE PATTERN"** HAS BEEN MOVED DOWN THE NECK TWO (2) FRETS (LOWER IN PITCH).

RIGHT - THE **"SCALE PATTERN"** HAS BEEN MOVED UP THE NECK TWO (2) FRETS (HIGHER IN PITCH).

(SEE PAGE 26 FOR MORE DETAIL)

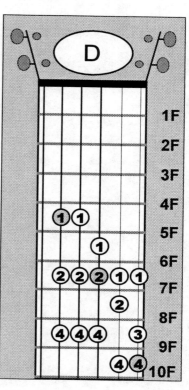

"C" Major Scale (Double Octave Scales)
(Optional Fingering)
Pattern 5-II & Pattern 3-I

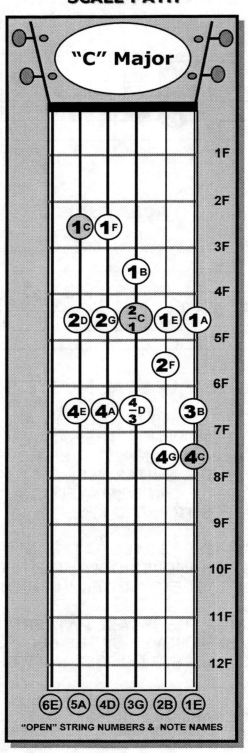

"SCALE PATH"

"C" Major Scale (Double Octave Scales)
(Optional Fingering)
Pattern 5-II & Pattern 3-I Standard Notation & Tablature

"STANDARD NOTATION"

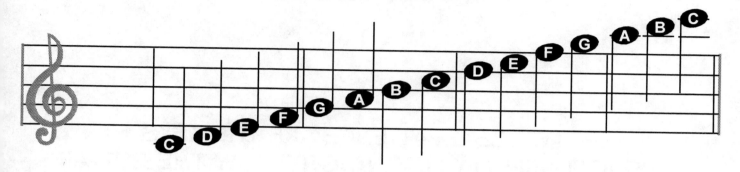

"TABLATURE"

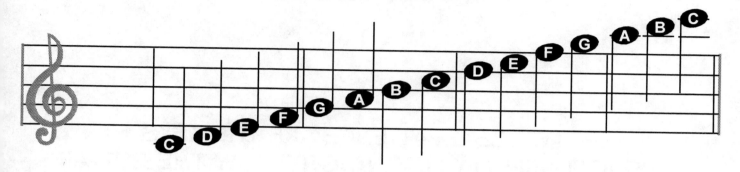

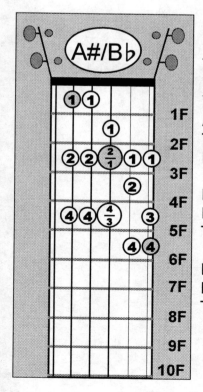

"MOVEABLE SCALE PATTERN"

THE DIAGRAMS TO THE LEFT AND RIGHT SHOW HOW THE SAME "SCALE PATTERN" CAN BE MOVED ALONG THE GUITAR NECK SO THAT THE SCALE CAN BE PLAYED IN A NEW POSITION AND KEY.

LEFT - THE "SCALE PATTERN" HAS BEEN MOVED DOWN THE NECK TWO (2) FRETS (LOWER IN PITCH).

RIGHT - THE "SCALE PATTERN" HAS BEEN MOVED UP THE NECK TWO (2) FRETS (HIGHER IN PITCH).

(SEE PAGE 26 FOR MORE DETAIL)

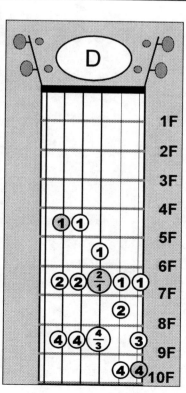

PRACTICE & PATIENCE ARE THE KEYS
TO SUCCESSFULLY LEARNING TO PLAY THE GUITAR

Part III

Major Pentatonic Scales
Minor Pentatonic Scale
The "Blues Scale"

ABOUT PENTATONIC SCALES

Penta means "five" and tonic means "tone." So, as the name implies, a **Pentatonic Scale** is a scale comprised of five (5) tones or notes. In the "Musical Universe," there are many variations of the **Pentatonic Scale,** however, we will just show you two (2) of the most popular and useful **Pentatonic Scales.** The **Pentatonic Scales** you are going to learn are almost "song-like" in quality when played, and are, in fact, the basis for many folk, blues, country and rock melodies. We will not go into the detail that we spent on the **Major Scales,** so we will keep it short and sweet.

The Major Pentatonic Scale

The **Major Pentatonic Scale** is just like the **Major Scale** with the exception that two (2) notes are omitted. The omitted notes are the fourth (4th) tone and the seventh (7th) tone of the **Major Scale.** All the other tones are present and accounted for. The Key of **"C" Major Pentatonic Scale** would look like this:

C - D - E - G - A - C (The **"F"** and **"B"** notes are omitted)

The Minor Pentatonic Scale

The **Minor Pentatonic Scale** is similar to a **Natural Minor Scale** (not covered in this book) with the exception of two (2) notes that are omitted from the **Natural Minor Scale** to create the **Minor Pentatonic Scale.** The omitted notes are the second (2nd) and sixth (6th) tones of the **Natural Minor Scale.** All the other notes are present and accounted for. The **Natural Minor Scale** will be covered in a later book.

The Key of **"A" Minor Pentatonic Scale** would look like this:

A - C - D - E - G - A (The **"B"** and **"F"** notes are omitted)

The Blues Scale

The **"Blues Scale"** is very similar to the **Minor Pentatonic Scale** with just one exception; the addition of the **"Flatted Fifth" Tone** (♭**V**). Because of this added note or tone, the **Blues Scale** is not a pentatonic scale because it now has six (6) notes instead of five (5). Here is how the **Blues Scale** in **"A"** would look like:

A - C - D - E♭ - E - G - A

The **"E♭"** gives this scale that very distinctive "blues sound." Another important feature of the **Blues Scale** is that the chords that are normally used (accompaniment) with this scale are the same chords that are normally used when playing a song or scale in a **Major Key.** This creates a very unique musical environment; **a Minor like scale played over Major (key) chords (harmony).**

"A" Major Pentatonic Scale
(Double Octave)
Pattern 6-I

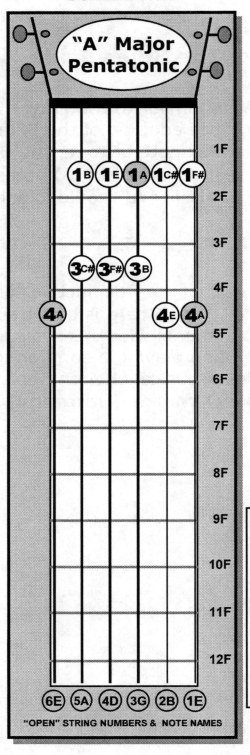

SEE OUR **"SCALE FINDER"**
ON PAGE 93 FOR ALL
SCALES THAT ARE BASED
ON THIS PATTERN.
REMEMBER,
THE FIRST NUMBER IN THE
SCALE **PATTERN NAME**
MEANS THAT THE
PATTERN STARTS ON
THAT NUMBERED STRING
ONLY!

76

"A" Major Pentatonic Scale
(Double Octave)
Pattern 6-I Standard Notation & Tablature

"STANDARD NOTATION"

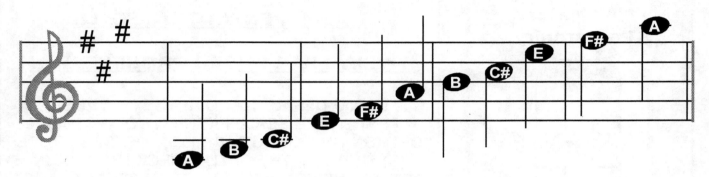

"TABLATURE"

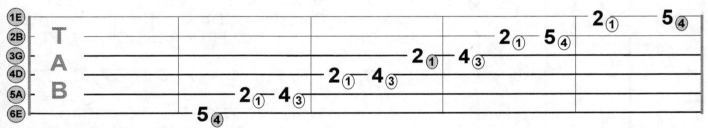

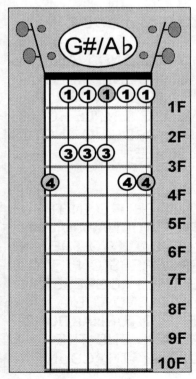

"MOVEABLE SCALE PATTERN"

THE DIAGRAMS TO THE LEFT AND RIGHT SHOW HOW THE SAME "SCALE PATTERN" CAN BE MOVED ALONG THE GUITAR NECK SO THAT THE SCALE CAN BE PLAYED IN A NEW POSITION AND KEY.

LEFT - THE "SCALE PATTERN" HAS BEEN MOVED DOWN THE NECK ONE (1) FRET (LOWER IN PITCH).

RIGHT - THE "SCALE PATTERN" HAS BEEN MOVED UP THE NECK THREE (3) FRETS (HIGHER IN PITCH).

(SEE PAGE 26 FOR MORE DETAIL)

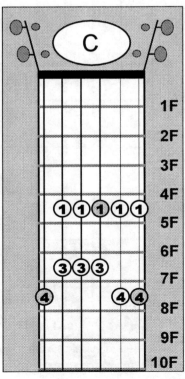

77

"A" Major Pentatonic Scale
(Double Octave)
Pattern 6-I

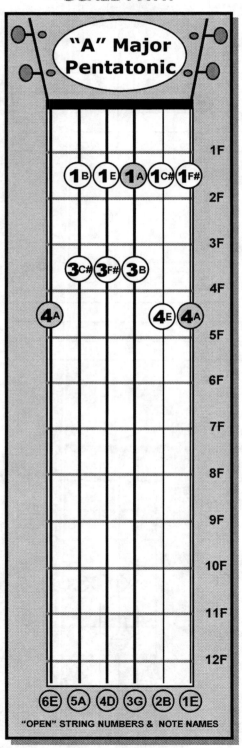

MAJOR PENTATONIC SCALE
&
TWELVE BAR CHORD PROGRESSION

IF YOU DESIRE TO MOVE THE "A" MAJOR PENTATONIC SCALE PATTERN TO ANOTHER POSITION ON THE GUITAR NECK, LET'S SAY THREE (3) FRETS UP THE GUITAR NECK (HIGHER IN PITCH), THE SCALE WOULD THEN BECOME A "C" MAJOR PENTATONIC SCALE. REMEMBER WHEN YOU CHANGE THE KEY OF THE SCALE, YOU MUST CHANGE THE CORRESPONDING CHORDS. IN THIS CASE, THE NEW CHORD PROGRESSION CAN BE:

C, F, C, C7, F, Fm, C, A7, D7, G7, C, G7

INFORMATION ABOUT CHANGING CHORD PATTERNS CAN BE FOUND IN:
THE "FIRST STAGE" GUITAR BOOK

REMEMBER, ONCE YOU MEMORIZE AND MASTER THE PENTATONIC PATTERNS CONTAINED IN THIS BOOK, YOU CAN USE THE NOTES IN THE **PENTATONIC SCALE** TO COMPOSE SIMPLE SONGS AND MELODIES BY VARYING THE ORDER OF NOTES PLAYED IN THE SCALE.

ON THE NEXT PAGE, THE LAST CHORD IN THE PROGRESSION IS CALLED THE "TURNAROUND" CHORD. IT WILL LEAD YOU BACK TO THE BEGINNING OF THE CHORD PROGRESSION IF YOU WANT TO CONTINUE PLAYING THE PROGRESSION. WHEN YOU ARE READY TO END THE PROGRESSION, CHANGE THE "E7" TURNAROUND CHORD TO AN "A" CHORD AND END THE PROGRESSION ON THE FOURTH (4TH) COUNT.

"A" Major Pentatonic Scale (Double Octave)
Twelve Bar Practice Chord Progression

The Staffs below are divided into four bars (measures) by vertical lines (called "Bar Lines"), and within each bar is a chord. Strum each chord you play at least four times, to a count of four. Try tapping your foot to keep count (1 anna 2 anna 3 anna 4). The "number" count is when your foot taps the floor, the "anna" count is when your foot is raised. You may wish to record this chord progression or have someone else play it while you practice the scale along with the chords. Some of the chords repeat. When this occurs, simply play that chord for four more counts. Repeat the progression after the 12th Chord, (Turnaround Chord).

<u>DO</u> <u>NOT</u> <u>PLAY</u> <u>BROKEN</u> <u>LINE</u> <u>STRINGS</u>, HOWEVER PLAY ALL OTHER STRINGS IN CHORDS

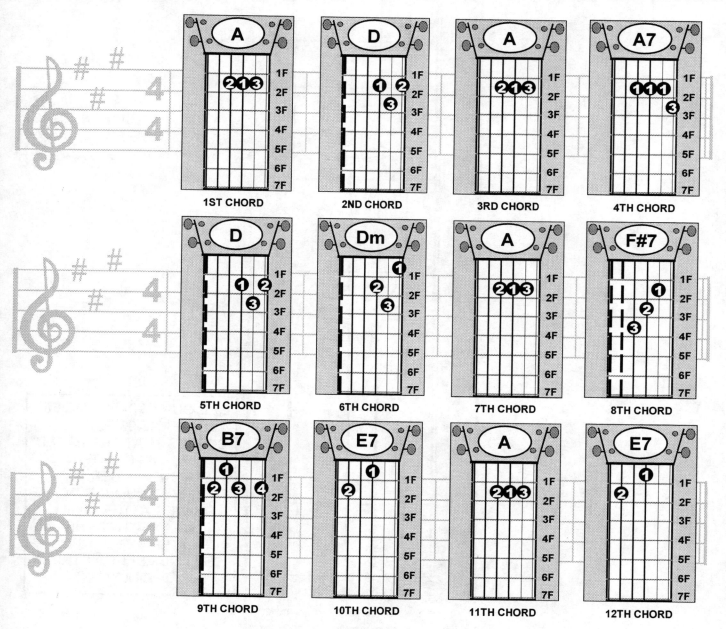

79

"A" Major Pentatonic Scale
(Double Octave)
Pattern 6-II

"SCALE PATH"

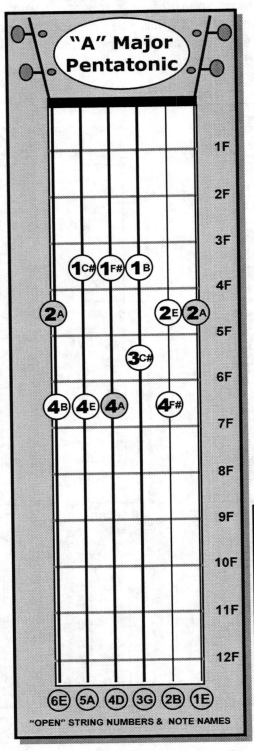

"A" Major Pentatonic

SEE OUR **"SCALE FINDER"** ON PAGE 93 FOR ALL SCALES THAT ARE BASED ON THIS PATTERN. REMEMBER, THE FIRST NUMBER IN THE SCALE **PATTERN NAME** MEANS THAT THE PATTERN STARTS ON THAT NUMBERED STRING ONLY!

80

"A" Major Pentatonic Scale
(Double Octave)
Pattern 6-II Standard Notation & Tablature

"STANDARD NOTATION"

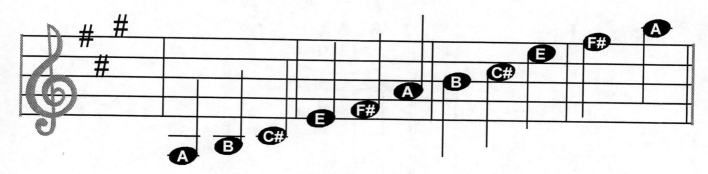

"TABLATURE"

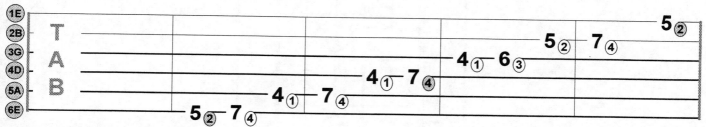

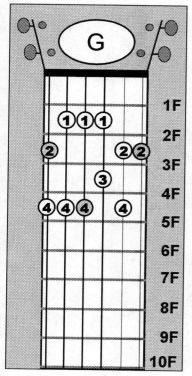

"MOVEABLE SCALE PATTERNS"

THE DIAGRAMS TO THE LEFT AND RIGHT SHOW HOW THE SAME "SCALE PATTERN" CAN BE MOVED ALONG THE GUITAR NECK SO THAT THE SCALE CAN BE PLAYED IN A NEW POSITION AND KEY.

LEFT - THE "SCALE PATTERN" HAS BEEN MOVED DOWN THE NECK TWO (2) FRETS (LOWER IN PITCH).

RIGHT - THE "SCALE PATTERN" HAS BEEN MOVED UP THE NECK THREE (3) FRETS (HIGHER IN PITCH).

(SEE PAGE 26 FOR MORE DETAIL)

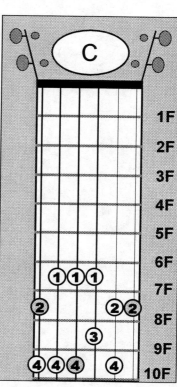

"A" Major Pentatonic Scale
(Double Octave)
Pattern 6-II

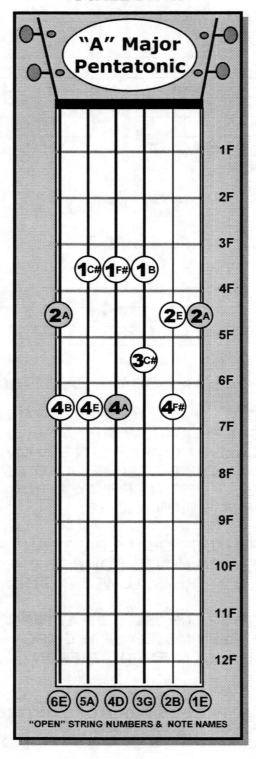

"A" Major Pentatonic Scale (Double Octave)
Twelve Bar Practice Chord Progression

The Staffs below are divided into four bars (measures) by vertical lines (called "Bar Lines"), and within each bar is a chord. Strum each chord you play at least four times, to a count of four. Try tapping your foot to keep count (1 anna 2 anna 3 anna 4). The "number" count is when your foot taps the floor, the "anna" count is when your foot is raised. You may wish to record this chord progression or have someone else play it while you practice the scale along with the chords. Some of the chords repeat. When this occurs, simply play that chord for four more counts. Repeat the progression after the 12th Chord, (Turnaround Chord).

<u>DO</u> <u>NOT</u> <u>PLAY</u> <u>BROKEN</u> <u>LINE</u> <u>STRINGS</u>, HOWEVER PLAY ALL OTHER STRINGS IN CHORDS

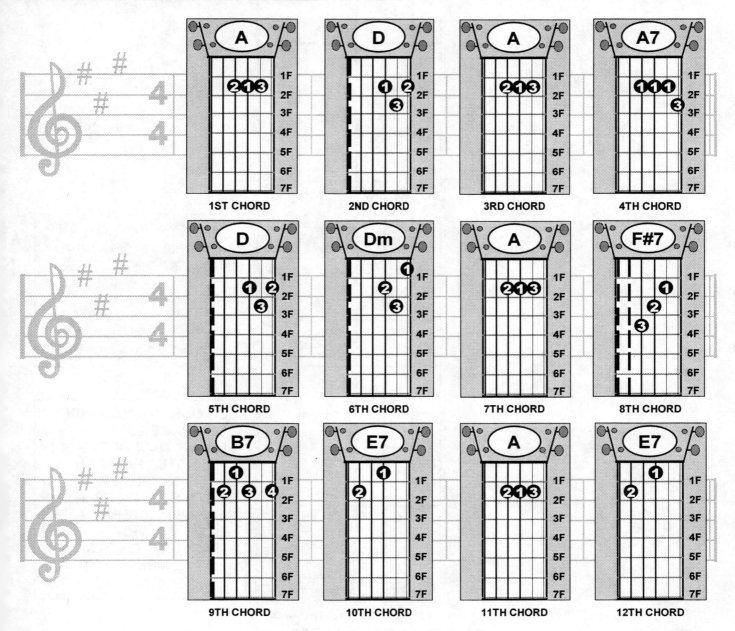

83

"A" Minor Pentatonic Scale
(Double Octave)
Pattern 6-I

"SCALE PATH"

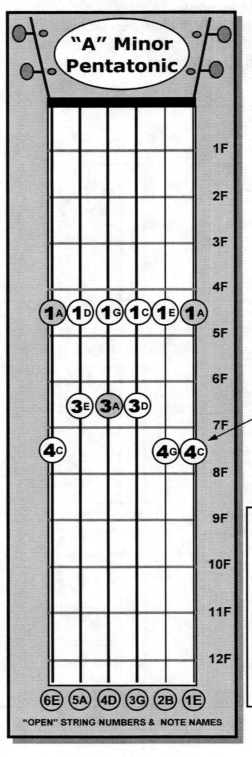

*THE "C" NOTE ON THE FIRST STRING, EIGHT FRET, IS AN OPTIONAL NOTE THAT IS ADDED ONE AND A HALF STEPS (3 FRETS) ABOVE THE ROOT NOTE "A."

SEE OUR **"SCALE FINDER"** ON PAGE 93 FOR ALL SCALES THAT ARE BASED ON THIS PATTERN. REMEMBER, THE FIRST NUMBER IN THE SCALE **PATTERN NAME** MEANS THAT THE PATTERN STARTS ON THAT NUMBERED STRING **ONLY!**

84

"A" Minor Pentatonic Scale
(Double Octave)
Pattern 6-I Standard Notation & Tablature

"STANDARD NOTATION"

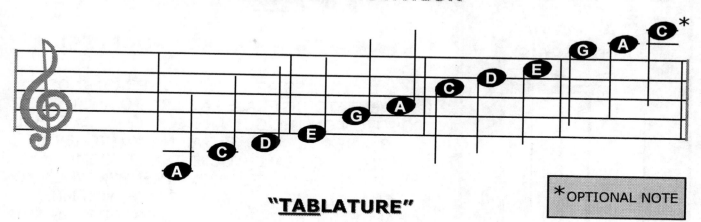

"TABLATURE"

*OPTIONAL NOTE

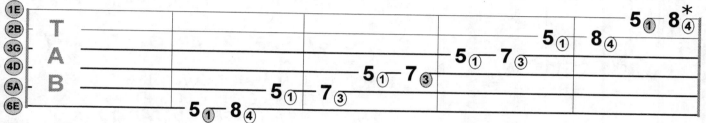

"MOVEABLE SCALE PATTERN"

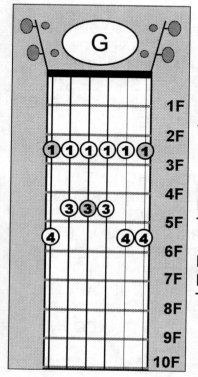

THE DIAGRAMS TO THE LEFT AND RIGHT SHOW HOW THE SAME "SCALE PATTERN" CAN BE MOVED ALONG THE GUITAR NECK SO THAT THE SCALE CAN BE PLAYED IN A NEW POSITION AND KEY.

LEFT - THE "SCALE PATTERN" HAS BEEN MOVED DOWN THE NECK TWO (2) FRETS (LOWER IN PITCH).

RIGHT - THE "SCALE PATTERN" HAS BEEN MOVED UP THE NECK TWO (2) FRETS (HIGHER IN PITCH).

(SEE PAGE 26 FOR MORE DETAIL)

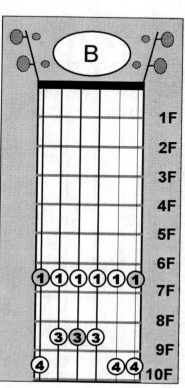

85

"A" Minor Pentatonic Scale
(Double Octave)
Pattern 6-I

"SCALE PATH"

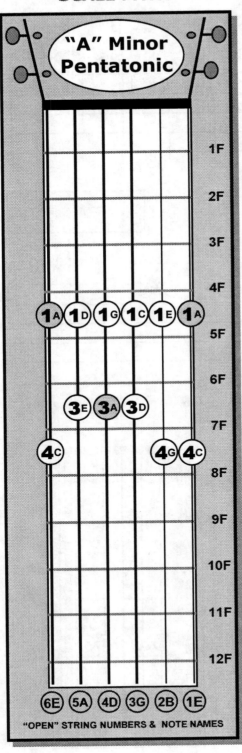

MINOR PENTATONIC SCALE
&
TWELVE BAR CHORD PROGRESSION

IF YOU DESIRE TO MOVE THE "A" MINOR PENTATONIC SCALE PATTERN TO ANOTHER POSITION ON THE GUITAR NECK, LET'S SAY THREE (3) FRETS UP THE GUITAR NECK (HIGHER IN PITCH), THE SCALE WOULD THEN BECOME A "C" MINOR PENTATONIC SCALE. REMEMBER WHEN YOU CHANGE THE KEY OF THE SCALE, YOU MUST CHANGE THE CORRESPONDING CHORDS. IN THIS CASE, THE NEW CHORD PROGRESSION CAN BE:

C, F, C, C7, F, F7, C, C7, G7, F, C, G7

INFORMATION ABOUT CHANGING CHORD PATTERNS CAN BE FOUND IN:
THE "FIRST STAGE" GUITAR BOOK

REMEMBER, ONCE YOU MEMORIZE AND MASTER THE PENTATONIC PATTERNS CONTAINED IN THIS BOOK, YOU CAN USE THE NOTES IN THE **PENTATONIC SCALE** TO COMPOSE SIMPLE SONGS AND MELODIES BY VARYING THE ORDER OF NOTES PLAYED IN THE SCALE.

ON THE NEXT PAGE, THE LAST CHORD IN THE PROGRESSION IS CALLED THE "TURNAROUND" CHORD. IT WILL LEAD YOU BACK TO THE BEGINNING OF THE CHORD PROGRESSION IF YOU WANT TO CONTINUE PLAYING THE PROGRESSION. WHEN YOU ARE READY TO END THE PROGRESSION, CHANGE THE "E7" TURNAROUND CHORD TO AN "A" CHORD AND END THE PROGRESSION ON THE FOURTH (4TH) COUNT.

"A" Minor Pentatonic Scale (Double Octave)
Twelve Bar Practice Chord Progression

The Staffs below are divided into four bars (measures) by vertical lines (called "Bar Lines"), and within each bar is a chord. Strum each chord you play at least four times, to a count of four. Try tapping your foot to keep count (1 anna 2 anna 3 anna 4). The "number" count is when your foot taps the floor, the "anna" count is when your foot is raised. You may wish to record this chord progression or have someone else play it while you practice the scale along with the chords. Some of the chords repeat. When this occurs, simply play that chord for four more counts. Repeat the progression after the 12th Chord, (Turnaround Chord).

<u>DO</u> <u>NOT</u> <u>PLAY</u> <u>BROKEN</u> <u>LINE</u> <u>STRINGS</u>, HOWEVER PLAY ALL OTHER STRINGS IN CHORDS

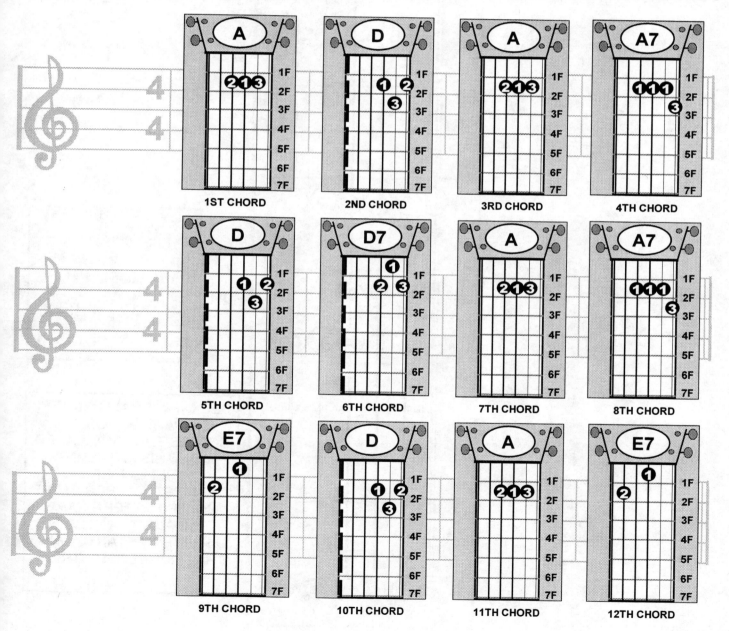

"Blues Scale" In "A"
(Double Octave)
(Based on the Minor Pentatonic Scale)

"SCALE PATH"

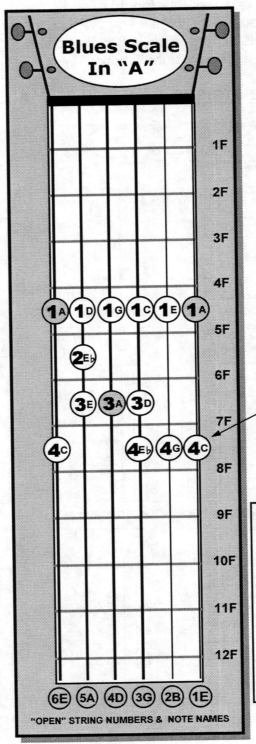

*THE "C" NOTE ON THE FIRST STRING, EIGHT FRET, IS AN <u>OPTIONAL</u> NOTE THAT IS ADDED ONE AND A HALF STEPS (3 FRETS) ABOVE THE ROOT NOTE "A."

SEE OUR **"SCALE FINDER"** ON PAGE 93 FOR ALL SCALES THAT ARE BASED ON THIS PATTERN. REMEMBER, THE FIRST NUMBER IN THE SCALE **PATTERN NAME** MEANS THAT THE PATTERN STARTS ON THAT NUMBERED STRING **ONLY!**

"Blues Scale" In "A"
(Double Octave)
Standard Notation & Tablature

"STANDARD NOTATION"

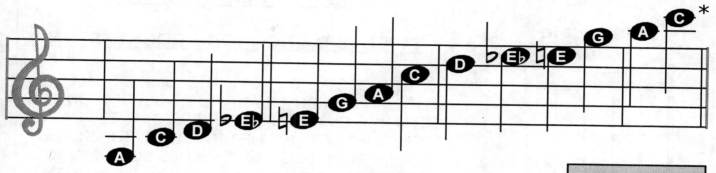

"TABLATURE"

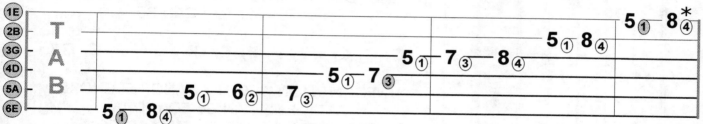

* OPTIONAL NOTE

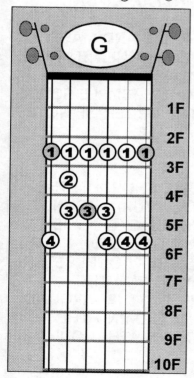

"MOVEABLE SCALE PATTERN"

THE DIAGRAMS TO THE LEFT AND RIGHT SHOW HOW THE SAME **"SCALE PATTERN"** CAN BE MOVED ALONG THE GUITAR NECK SO THAT THE SCALE CAN BE PLAYED IN A NEW POSITION AND KEY.

LEFT - THE **"SCALE PATTERN"** HAS BEEN MOVED DOWN THE NECK TWO (2) FRETS (LOWER IN PITCH).

RIGHT - THE **"SCALE PATTERN"** HAS BEEN MOVED UP THE NECK TWO (2) FRETS (HIGHER IN PITCH).

(SEE PAGE 26 FOR MORE DETAIL)

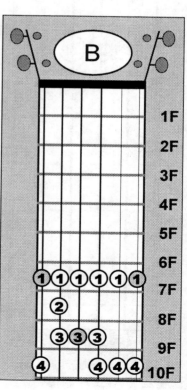

89

"Blues Scale" In "A"
(Double Octave)
(Based on the Minor Pentatonic Scale)

"SCALE PATH"

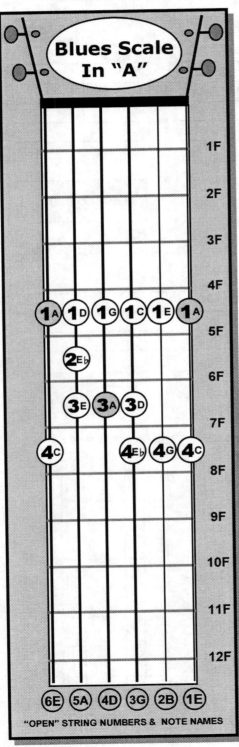

"OPEN" STRING NUMBERS & NOTE NAMES

"BLUES SCALE" IN "A"
&
TWELVE BAR CHORD PROGRESSION

IF YOU DESIRE TO MOVE THE "BLUES SCALE" IN THE "A" PATTERN TO ANOTHER POSITION ON THE GUITAR NECK, LET'S SAY THREE (3) FRETS UP THE GUITAR NECK (HIGHER IN PITCH), THE SCALE WOULD THEN BECOME A "BLUES SCALE" IN "C". REMEMBER WHEN YOU CHANGE THE KEY OF THE SCALE, YOU MUST CHANGE THE CORRESPONDING CHORDS. IN THIS CASE, THE NEW CHORD PROGRESSION CAN BE:

C, C, C, C7, F, F, C, C7, G7, F, C, G7

INFORMATION ABOUT CHANGING CHORD PATTERNS CAN BE FOUND IN:
THE "FIRST STAGE" GUITAR BOOK

REMEMBER, ONCE YOU MEMORIZE AND MASTER THE PENTATONIC PATTERNS CONTAINED IN THIS BOOK, YOU CAN USE THE NOTES IN THE **PENTATONIC SCALE** TO COMPOSE SIMPLE SONGS AND MELODIES BY VARYING THE ORDER OF NOTES PLAYED IN THE SCALE.

ON THE NEXT PAGE, THE LAST CHORD IN THE PROGRESSION IS CALLED THE "TURNAROUND" CHORD. IT WILL LEAD YOU BACK TO THE BEGINNING OF THE CHORD PROGRESSION IF YOU WANT TO CONTINUE PLAYING THE PROGRESSION. WHEN YOU ARE READY TO END THE PROGRESSION, CHANGE THE "E7" TURNAROUND CHORD TO AN "A" CHORD AND END THE PROGRESSION ON THE FOURTH (4TH) COUNT.

90

"Blues Scale" In "A" (Double Octave)
Twelve Bar Practice Chord Progression

The Staffs below are divided into four bars (measures) by vertical lines (called "Bar Lines"), and within each bar is a chord. Strum each chord you play at least four times, to a count of four. Try tapping your foot to keep count (1 anna 2 anna 3 anna 4). The "number" count is when your foot taps the floor, the "anna" count is when your foot is raised. You may wish to record this chord progression or have someone else play it while you practice the scale along with the chords. Some of the chords repeat. When this occurs, simply play that chord for four more counts. Repeat the progression after the 12th Chord, (Turnaround Chord).

<u>YOU CAN SUBSTITUTE THE "D9th" CHORD FOR THE "D" CHORD & THE "E9th" FOR THE "E7th"</u>
<u>DO</u> <u>NOT</u> <u>PLAY</u> BROKEN <u>LINE</u> STRINGS, HOWEVER PLAY ALL OTHER STRINGS IN CHORDS

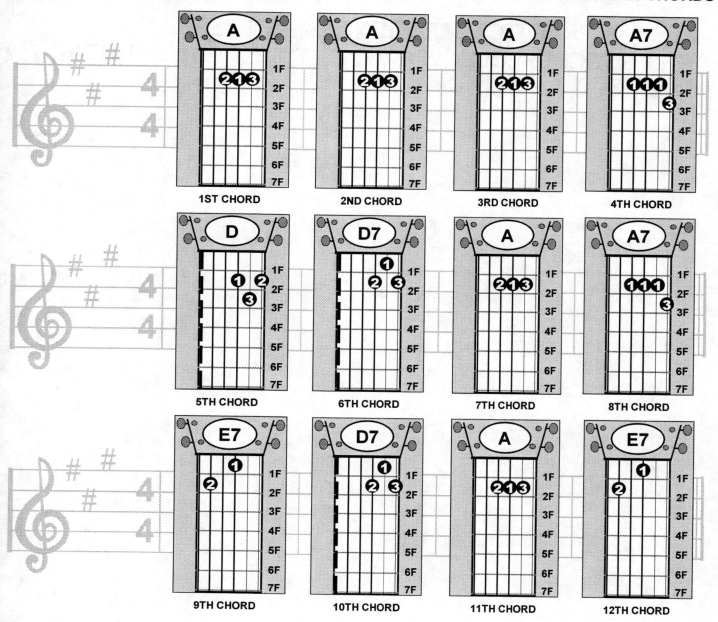

PRACTICE & PATIENCE ARE THE KEYS
TO SUCCESSFULLY LEARNING TO PLAY THE GUITAR

SCALE FINDER

THIS PATTERN IS ON PAGE 76

Major Pentatonic PATTERN 6-I	
*Starting Fret	Scale Name
4	G#/A♭
5	A
6	A#/B♭
7	B
8	C
9	C#/D♭
10	D
11	D#/E♭
12	E
13	F
14	F#/G♭

THIS PATTERN IS ON PAGE 80

Major Pentatonic PATTERN 6-II	
*Starting Fret	Scale Name
2	F#/G♭
3	G
4	G#/A♭
5	A
6	A#/B♭
7	B
8	C
9	C#/D♭
10	D
11	D#/E♭
12	E
13	F

*The "Starting Fret" = Circled "Root" Note In The "Scale Path" Diagram

THIS PATTERN IS ON PAGE 84

Minor Pentatonic (Only One Pattern)	
*Starting Fret	Scale Name
1	F
2	F#/G♭
3	G
4	G#/A♭
5	A
6	A#/B♭
7	B
8	C
9	C#/D♭
10	D
11	D#/E♭
12	E

THIS PATTERN IS ON PAGE 88

BLUES Scale (Only One Pattern)	
*Starting Fret	Scale Name
1	F
2	F#/G♭
3	G
4	G#/A♭
5	A
6	A#/B♭
7	B
8	C
9	C#/D♭
10	D
11	D#/E♭
12	E

PRACTICE & PATIENCE ARE THE KEYS
TO SUCCESSFULLY LEARNING TO PLAY THE GUITAR

MORE "HOW TO PLAY GUITAR" BOOKS

ON ANOTHER NOTE,
IF YOU WOULD LIKE TO LEARN HOW TO PLAY THE MOST COMMONLY PLAYED GUITAR CHORDS
ALONG WITH A LOT OF OTHER VERY HELPFUL AND USEFUL INFORMATION, SUCH AS FORMING
CHORD PROGRESSIONS, ETC., BE SURE TO GET A COPY OF:

THE "FIRST STAGE" GUITAR BOOK -
LEARN HOW TO PLAY GUITAR EASILY & QUICKLY!

OR

THE "GUITAR BOOK" -
FOR THOSE WHO HAVE JUST LANDED ON THE PLANET EARTH! - LEARN HOW TO PLAY GUITAR

BOTH THE "FIRST STAGE" GUITAR BOOK AND THE "GUITAR BOOK"... CONTAIN THE SAME LEARN
HOW TO PLAY GUITAR INFORMATION COVERING THE MOST COMMONLY PLAYED "OPEN" GUITAR
CHORDS, "BARRE" CHORDS, "9TH" CHORDS, "7TH" CHORDS IN BOLD DIAGRAMS AND LOTS MORE!
(THE ONLY DIFFERENCE IS YOU GET A CHOICE OF WHICH BOOK COVER YOU WOULD PREFER)

ALSO AVAILABLE IS THE QUICK CHORD REFERENCE CHART:

THE "FIRST STAGE" GUITAR CHORD CHART -
LEARN HOW TO PLAY THE MOST COMMONLY PLAYED GUITAR CHORDS!

A CONVENIENTLY HANDY REFERENCE GUIDE FOR THE BEGINNING GUITAR PLAYER AND LOTS
MORE!

COMING SOON!!...MORE COLORFUL SCALES, MODES, AND COMPLIMENTARY
CHORD PROGRESSIONS.....TO BE INTRODUCED IN A LATER GUITAR BOOK WHICH
WILL BE CALLED:

THE "ON STAGE" GUITAR BOOK -
LEARN HOW TO PLAY SCALE PATTERNS ON CHORDS EASILY & QUICKLY!

For more information about these other guitar learning items, visit Web Site at:

www.QUICKSTARTGUITAR.com

or write to:

Christopher Winkle Products
Attn: Chris Lopez
P.O. Box 1898
Lomita, CA 90717
USA

E-mail: quickstartguitar@msn.com

CUSTOMER MAIL-IN REVIEW PAGE
(Simply Remove This Page From Book And Mail)

**We would appreciate hearing from you and knowing how you like the book.
Your review would be greatly appreciated.**

**We would like very much to have your review posted at various book selling locations.
Please fill out the following information and return to address indicated below.
You can also submit this information via E-mail at the address below.**

Your Name:	
Your Address:	
City:	
State:	**Zip Code:**
Your E-mail Address:	

It is necessary to include your E-mail address
Your E-mail address will not be posted when it is submitted to review locations

The "Next Stage" Guitar Book.....
YOUR REVIEW & 5 STAR RATING:

WRITE A HEADLINE FOR YOUR REVIEW:

_____

YOUR REVIEW:

_____
_____
_____
_____
_____

Circle The Number You Rate This Book: 1 2 3 4 5
(**1** Being The Lowest Rating & **5** Being The Highest Rating)

www.QUICKSTARTGUITAR.com

Please forward your review to this address:

**Christopher Winkle Products
Attn: "QuickStartGuitar"
P.O. Box 1898
Lomita, CA 90717
USA**

or

E-mail your review information to:

quickstartguitar@msn.com